A CATALOGUE
OF THE
FREDERICK W. & CARRIE S. BEINECKE
COLLECTION OF
WESTERN AMERICANA

VOLUME ONE: MANUSCRIPTS

Frederick W. Beinecke

A CATALOGUE
OF THE
FREDERICK W. & CARRIE S. BEINECKE
COLLECTION OF
WESTERN AMERICANA

VOLUME ONE: MANUSCRIPTS

COMPILED BY JEANNE M. GODDARD AND CHARLES KRITZLER

AND EDITED WITH AN INTRODUCTION BY ARCHIBALD HANNA

NEW HAVEN AND LONDON, YALE UNIVERSITY PRESS, 1965

TO CARRIE SPERRY BEINECKE

WITH THE AFFECTION OF THE

EDITORS AND COMPILERS

FACSIMILES

The manuscripts reproduced in facsimile have been chosen not on the basis of textual importance but to provide scholars with examples of the handwriting of persons important to the history of the West, whose manuscripts are not readily available in most research libraries for comparison.

INTRODUCTION

In 1952 the Yale Collection of Western Americana first opened its doors to the public. Yale already had substantial holdings in this field, notably Henry R. Wagner's Texas and Middle West collection and the Walter B. McClintock collection on the Blackfoot Indians. The gift of William Robertson Coe's magnificent Western Americana Collection, which came to Yale over a period of years beginning in 1942, and the Pacific Northwest Collection formed by Winlock Miller, Jr., Yale 1928, given by his father in 1948, brought Yale into the front rank in this important area of American history. Moreover, Mr. Coe's generous endowment of his collection made it possible to bring together in one place most of the University's scattered holdings of rare books and manuscripts in this field, not only to ensure their physical preservation but also to make them more easily available to scholars. And in 1952, the Yale University Press published Mary C. Withington's *Catalogue of Manuscripts in the Collection of Western Americana founded by William Robertson Coe.*

Miss Withington's catalogue was, of course, out of date on the day it was published. In the ensuing years the Yale Collection of Western Americana has continued to grow until it is now more than double its size at that time. To each of the individual collections it has been possible to add books and manuscripts thanks to the endowments which their donors provided. And in 1956 the generosity of many friends of the library made it possible to acquire the great Texas Collection formed by Thomas W. Streeter. But the major factor in this great increase of strength in Western Americana at Yale has been the formation and growth of the Frederick W. and Carrie S. Beinecke Collection.

Mr. Beinecke came late to book collecting. For many years the multitudinous demands of his wide-ranging business affairs left little leisure for other pursuits. It was not surprising that so vigorous an entrepreneur should develop an interest in the American West, where individual initiative has counted for more than in perhaps any other region of this continent. He read widely, both popular works and scholarly histories. And when at last he was able to turn over some of his administrative responsibilities to younger hands, his long-dormant collector's instinct awoke.

In the early nineteen-fifties, when Mr. Beinecke began his career as a serious collector, there were not wanting those who believed that the great days of Western Americana were already over and that it was no longer possible to assemble a really great collection in this area. Time has proved them wrong. In little more than a decade, the Beinecke Collection has grown in size and significance of content to a point where it may fairly claim to be listed among the great collections of Western Americana.

Although the range of Mr. Beinecke's collecting interest has been wide, embracing the whole of the trans-Mississippi West, the major emphasis has been on the Spanish Southwest and California, from the period of discovery and exploration by the Spanish down through the Mexican War and the gold rush. This was the area in which the Yale collections were weakest, a fact which has strongly influenced Mr. Beinecke's collecting policy. Though the building of this great research collection is only one among his many benefactions to the University from which he graduated in 1909 in the Sheffield Scientific School, a librarian will be pardoned for counting it among the greatest.

Mr. Beinecke's desire that the results of his collecting should further the work of historians not only at Yale but throughout the scholarly community has led to the publication of this catalogue of his collection. Because the collection is still growing, it has seemed best to devote the first volume to manuscripts, as being of the most immediate value to scholars. Subsequent volumes will describe the printed books, pamphlets and broadsides, and a final volume will be devoted to those manuscripts acquired or catalogued subsequent to the publication of this first volume.

The manuscripts listed in this catalogue have been arranged alphabetically by author, or in a few cases by the collector or subject of a group of manuscripts. Standard library practice has been followed in entering official documents and correspondence under the name of the office rather than the individual (e.g., U.S. War Dept. rather than Floyd, John B.). The index, however, contains in each case a reference from the person's name not only to the manuscript but also to any offices held by the man.

Each numbered entry contains an author or subject entry; a title, quoted if the manuscript itself bears a title; collation, including pagination, illustrative material when present, and size; a note about the author and a brief description of the scope and subject of the manuscript or group of manuscripts. Information about provenance or publication is given where known. The bracketed designation at the end of the entry is the call number under which the manuscript is presently shelved in the Beinecke Rare Book and Manuscript Library.

Although the index is as detailed as possible, no effort has been made to include every person or place mentioned in every manuscript. All authors of documents, leaves or letters are included, with cross references to official headings; the recipients of all letters, names of persons or places frequently mentioned whether listed in the entry or not, the names of ships, etc. For other subjects we have followed as closely as possible the Library of Congress list of subject headings.

Most of this catalogue is the work of Miss Jeanne M. Goddard, whose tireless and devoted labors over a three-year period now see their fruition. She was ably assisted during a part of that time by Mr. Charles Kritzler. My own part has been simply to offer aid and encouragement when needed, to supply an occasional phrase or piece of information, and to exercise a general supervision in the interest of stylistic uniformity. Whatever is well done belongs to them; what is amiss must be laid at my door.

ARCHIBALD HANNA, JR.

CATALOGUE

1 ACEVEDO, JUAN

Letter addressed to Manuel Isaac Gonzalez, governor of the State of Mexico. Teposcolula, Department of Huasuapam de Leon, Mexico, January 28, 1848.

2 pp. 27½ cm.

Informs Gonzalez of recent movements of the Mexican and American forces and newspaper reports of growing opposition to Santa Anna in the central Mexican States.

[S–772]

2 ADAMS, BENJAMIN F., *d.* 1849

Correspondence and papers, 1849–1850.

25 pp. 24–27 cm.

Adams was a member of the Ashtabula Company, which left Ohio for California overland in 1849, but he died of fever when only one hundred miles out on the trail. The letters deal primarily with the preparations for an overland journey to the Pacific and the circumstances surrounding his death. The latter correspondence, mostly written by Dr. Samuel Mathews, another member of the Ashtabula Company, includes a diagnosis of the causes of death, location of the grave, and an inventory of personal effects, with the disposition made of these. Included also are several letters of recommendation.

[S–689; Ad 17]

3 ALBIÇURI, JUAN

"Historia de la vida y martirio del venerable P. Hernando de Santaren de la compania de Jesus y de las cinco missiones apostolicas que fundo de Guazave, Topia, S Andres, Tecuchuapa y Xiximes por el P Juan de Albicuri, sacerdote de la misma compania y misionero en la mission de Topia." Topia, Mexico [*ca.* 1634].

643 pp. 22 cm.

Late in the 1500s Father Santaren left Huete, Spain, to come to the Mexican missions in the Province of Sinaloa. This biography of him, written by a member of the same Society, is divided into five books, beginning with Santaren's education and religious activities which he promoted, and concluding with his pious qualities. After arriving in Mexico, he went to Pueblo for a short time and then went north to Topia (Tamazula) in the province of Sinaloa. He showed great skill and diplomacy in converting the wild cannibalistic Indian tribes of the North—particularly the Yaquimi, Xiximes, Tecuchuapa, and Tepehuanes —to the Catholic Faith, and inspiring in them loyalty to the King of Spain. His work also brought him into contact with miners and secular officials. Urdiñola, governor of Sinaloa, sent Santaren to settle the disputes between the Spanish miners and the Acaxee Indians. Santaren was also put in charge of governing the college and missions at Sinaloa.

Although personally popular with the

Indians, Father Santaren, together with other missionaries, was murdered in an outbreak in November 1616. This life was undoubtedly composed as part of a campaign for his canonization.

According to José Gutierrez Casillas, the manuscript was formerly in the possession of Carlos Linga.

A printed biographical sketch by Catherine Mary McShane laid in.

[S–769]

4 ATCHISON, DAVID RICE, 1807–1886

Letter to the Honorable William J. Brown. Platte City, Missouri, August 10, 1845.

1 p. 25 cm. With address.

Recommending the appointment of Daniel Kelso to the Osage River Sub-agency. The principal interest is in the postscript which expresses the determination of the frontiersmen to secure California for the U.S., by force if necessary.

[S–690; At 24]

5 BAKER, M. L.

Three letters written to members of his family while he was in the army in Santa Fé, New Mexico, and Fort Leavenworth, Kansas, September 13, 1846, to April 28, 1847.

10 pp. 25 cm.

Baker, a corporal in B Troop, 1st Dragoons, took part in Kearny's expedition to Santa Fé. His letter to his sister describes the city and the life and customs of the New Mexicans. When Kearny left Santa Fé, B Troop was broken up, and the men distributed among the other troops. The officers went East on recruiting duty, and Baker returned to Fort Leavenworth to train recruits. His letters to his nephew describe the return trip, a brush with the Comanches, and the routine of dragoon life at a frontier post.

—— Letter to his sister, Mrs. Hugh Martin. Santa Fé, New Mexico, September 13, 1846. 3 pp.

—— Two letters to his nephew, M. Lee Baker Martin. Fort Leavenworth, Kansas, December 13, 1846, and April 28, 1847. 7 pp.

[S–502; B175]

6 BALLOU, MARY BEAN (SIMONDS), 1809–1894

Journal, 1851–1852.

[29] pp. 16 × 8½ cm.

Description of the voyage to California via Panama and life in the mines from a woman's point of view. The journal occupies pages [1]–[8] of a notebook and is followed by a letter to her sons, Selden and Augustus. Published as Mr. Beinecke's Christmas keepsake, December 1962: *I Hear the Hogs in My Kitchen.*

[S–681]

7 BALTHASAR, JUAN ANTONIO, 1697–1763

"Información de los Padres de la Prov^a de Cinaloa." Durango, Mexico, March 1745.

8 pp. 21½ cm.

A critical report on the qualifications, character, and conduct of the priests in each mission. A translation of this document, *Father Balthasar Visits the Sinaloa Missions, 1744–1745,* was printed as Beinecke's Christmas keepsake for 1959.

[S–637]

8 BALTHASAR, JUAN ANTONIO, 1697–1763

"Información de los Padres missioneros de la Prov^a de Sonora, como se hablan, al acabar esta visita del año 1744."

16 pp. 21 cm. Signed: Juan Anto° Balthasar.

A report similar to the above on the missionaries in Sonora, together with general comments on the Province, and a discussion of the advisability of dividing the provinces of Sonora and Sinaloa for more efficient administration.

[S–50]

9 BALTHASAR, JUAN ANTONIO, 1697–1763

Letter to "Mi Padre Provincial." Torin, Mexico, February 29, 1744.

2 pp. 21 cm.

Father Balthasar recommends that Lorenzo García be removed from his mission because he lacks knowledge of the country and the Indian languages.

[S–631]

10 BALTHASAR, JUAN ANTONIO, 1697–1763

"Visita de la Provincia de Sinaloa hecha por el P^e Visitador General Juan Antonio Balthasar en los años de 1743 de 1744."

33 pp. 21½ cm.

Juan Antonio Balthasar, a native of Lucerne, entered the Jesuit order at the age of fifteen. He was transferred to the Mexican Province and served successively as missionary, Rector of Colegio San Gregorio in Mexico City, Visitador to the missions in Sinaloa, Sonora, and California, and eventually Provincial of Mexico.

This report gives a detailed account of the expenses, debts, property, and number of families at each of the twenty-four missions in the province of Sinaloa.

[S–636]

11 BARNARD, FREDERIC W., *d.* 1857

Seven letters to his family from various places during the period March 22, 1849, to October 11, 1854.

28 pp. 25 cm.

These seven letters to various members of Barnard's family describe his trip from New York State to California and life at Marysville, California.

[S–680; B254]

12 BARNARD, MOSES J.

Journal of his trip to California by way of Panama, 1850.

35 pp. 24½ cm.

An account of a journey to San Francisco by way of Panama, describing the harbor fortifications of Chagres, Panama, and Realejo, Nicaragua. At Panama he became involved in a plot to overthrow the local government. Arriving in San Francisco, he describes the city in glowing terms, and completes the journal with a detailed description of the El Dorado Saloon. Included are copies of letters of recommendation written to help Barnard obtain a consulship.

[S–679; B255]

13 BERDUSCO, FRANCISCO, *defendant*

"Criminal contra D. Francisco Berdusco por tramar revolucion contra el govierno del territorio de la Alta California, para colocar en el al Senor D. José María Hijar. Juez Fiscal el Ten^te Ejército cuidadano el todo Santiago Gomez." Monterey, San Francisco, California, etc., February–December 1835.

273 pp. 20½–31 cm. On spine: Figueroa papers. Includes a list of individual letters and a typed calendar in English.

Complete proceedings of the trial of Francisco Berdusco including letters and testimony taken in the case against him for plotting the overthrow of the Figueroa government.

Figueroa came to Alta California with ten friars who were from the College of Zacatecas. Almost upon arrival, Figueroa requested retirement because of ill health; his petition was granted May 1833. This, therefore, was an opportune time for Berdusco to get the Mexican government to put José María Hijar in power.

Hijar collaborated with José María Padrés in a scheme to colonize Alta California as well as secularize the missions, the wealth derived to personally benefit both men. The Mexican government agreed to this project, since they were interested in promoting the Californias.

After a short delay, Hijar and Padrés arrived in California with the colonists, who had been induced to settle in Alta California by government promises of an allowance in pay, implements, seed, and domestic animals.

In the meantime, the Mexican government, under a new president who was distrustful of the Hijar and Padrés project, sent a messenger to Figueroa to remain in office and not to turn over the reigns of the government. By March 1835 Hijar and Padrés were returned to Mexico.

In his short term of office, Figueroa accomplished more than most governors, and was one of the most important figures in California history. He was also interested in colonizing California and developing its natural resources.

[S–574]

14 BIGLER, JOHN, 1805–1871

Letter to the President-elect of the United States [Pierce]. Vallejo, California, January 27, 1853.

1 p., docketed. 25 cm.

Recommending the services of Colonel Franklin Stewart to President-elect Pierce, outlining the contributions Stewart made toward Democratic victory in the election of 1852.

[S–780; B485]

15 ——, BILL

Letter to "Dear Nell." San Francisco, California, July 12, 1854.

6 pp. 24½ cm.

The peculiarities of a Chinese bath house and the celebration of the Fourth of July in San Francisco are described.

[S–687; B494]

16 BLANCHARD, GEORGE B.

Letter to his parents. San Francisco, California, September 14, 1852.

4 pp. 25 cm.

Blanchard relates his experiences on a 187-day voyage from Panama to San Francisco, starting aboard the bark *Emily* and finishing aboard the *Archibald Gracie*. He tells of the refusal of the *Emily*'s captain to continue with passengers because of the impossibility of reprovisioning the ship at San Blas, Mexico, and the subsequent negotiations with the American consul to advance funds to the captain for the chartering of another vessel. Conditions on both ships were bad, with short rations, sickness, and death beginning almost immediately. A fragment of another letter to his family is included, listing those who died during the voyages, and warning others not to follow.

[S–676; B592]

17 BLANQUEL, JOSEPH BERNABE

Letter to "Exmo Señor." San Ignacio, Sinaloa, Mexico, May 25, 1718.

4 pp. 30½ cm.

Blanquel requests that his superior allow the old padre, Marcel de Leon, to remain, contrary to custom, among the Indians in San Ignacio and San Augustin, Sinaloa, where he is greatly esteemed.

[S–626]

18 BLENNERHASSETT, HORATIO N.

Letter to Samuel Lyon. San Francisco, California, August 28, 1849.

3 pp. 25½ cm.

Writing to his friend of long standing, Blennerhassett describes his long and perilous voyage around the Horn, where he witnessed the sinking of three ships in a gale, "unable to give any assistance." At the time of the writing, he has returned

to San Francisco from his mining operations fifty miles from Sacramento City to
reprovision. Included is a description of
the construction of his mining apparatus,
the prices of food and lodging in San
Francisco, and some of the success he has
had at the mines. Written crossed, in
black and red.

[S–678; B617]

19 BLISS, WILLIAM WALLACE SMITH, *d.* 1853

Letter to Lieutenant D. McPhail, 5th Infantry. Matamoras, Mexico,
May 20, [1846].

1 p. 21 cm.

Instructions to McPhail for disposition of
his detachment of recruits. Bliss was Zachary Taylor's son-in-law and served as his
adjutant during the Mexican War.

[S–504; B619]

20 BONNER, B. LORING

Letter written by B. L. Bonner, an engineer in the 1st Division, to his
mother, Mrs. R. M. Bonner. Puebla, Mexico, July 27, 1847.

3 pp. 32 cm.

Contains a discussion of the peace negotiations and a description of Puebla.

[S–505; B643]

21 BOURKE, JOHN GREGORY, 1846–1896, *recipient*

Letters and papers, 1886–1899.

86 pp. 8–30½ cm.

Bourke, a captain in the 3d Cavalry,
served under General Crook in various
Indian campaigns in the Southwest. An
amateur ethnologist of some distinction,
he became well-known through his writ-
ings on Southwestern Indians. The present group consists mainly of letters to
Bourke from various scholars interested
in Indian affairs.

BANDELIER, ADOLPH FRANCIS ALPHONSE.
Typewritten letter to "My dear Captain."
April 9, 1888. 1 p.

BOAZ, FRANZ. Typewritten letter to
Bourke. June 27, 1891. 1 p.

BYWATER, MAURICE JAMES. Letter to
Bourke. October 29, 1888. 4 pp.

CROOK, GEORGE. Letter to "My dear
Bourke." November 20, 1888. 2 pp.

GILDER, WILLIAM HENRY. Letter to
Bourke. October 15, 1889. 8 pp.

HALE, EDWARD EVERETT. Letter to
Bourke. May 15, 1895. 2 pp.

HOWE, JOHN D. Typewritten unsigned
letter to Bourke. March 26, 1894. 1 p.

LANIER, HENRY WYSHAM. Letter to
Bourke. January 4, 1895. 3 pp.

LEAL, ALBERTO. Letter to Bourke. December 30, 1893. 1 p.

LUDINGTON, HORACE. Letter to "My dear
Captain." November 8, 1893. 1 p.

RODEN, CHARLES. Letter to Bourke. November 20, 1893. 2 pp.

ROOSEVELT, THEODORE. Typewritten letter to Bourke. January 12, 1895. 1 p.

STICKNEY, GARDNER P. Letter to Bourke.
June 17, 1893. 2 pp.

THATCHER, JOHN BOYD. Typewritten letter to Bourke. June 17, 1893. 1 p.

TRU, LAMBERT. Letter to Bourke. February 9, 1889. 3 pp.

WOODHEAD, J. E. Letter to Bourke. July 1, 1893. 2 pp.

WURTZ, GEORGE W. Letter to Bourke. June 20, 1889. 2 pp.

[S–881; B667]

22 BOURNE, JULIA A. G.

Letter to "My dear friends." Stockton, California, June 2, 1856.

6 pp. 25 cm.

Arriving in San Francisco at the time of the funeral of James King of William, Mrs. Bourne describes the city in mourning and the scene of the hangings of his murderer and that of Charles Cora, the murderer of Colonel Richardson. The remainder of her letter describes Stockton and life there, with some comments on ladies' fashions.

[S–736; B667]

23 BRADFORD, EDMUND, d. 1889

Seven letters to his sister, Caroline Bradford, and to his father-in-law, John N. Tazewell. Various places, September 24, 1846, to May 19, 1848.

30 pp. 25–32½ cm.

Bradford, a lieutenant in the 4th Artillery, gives detailed accounts of the battles of Monterrey and Vera Cruz, in which he participated, and of the quarrels between Scott and his subordinates at the close of the War.

[S–650; B728]

24 BRANNAN, SAMUEL, 1819–1889

Letter written to the San Francisco Town Council. San Francisco, California, October 7, 1847.

Requests the council to delay action on the ouster of Alcalde George Hyde so that Brannan may be present at the hearing.

[S–677; B735]

25 BROOKS, SUMNER CUMMINGS

Ten letters written by Sumner Cummings Brooks while he was in the army to his parents [Charlotte N. and Levi Sargent]. Various places, June 22, 1845, to December 2, 1848.

23 pp. 24–32 cm.

The letters trace his career in the Army from his enlistment in Boston, to Fort Constitution, New Hampshire, and the March from Corpus Christi to the Rio Grande. He tells of the battles of the Rio Grande, the capture of Matamoras, and the battle of Monterrey. Brooks leaves Taylor's army and joins General Scott at the siege of Vera Cruz. He gives an exellent description of the battle and capture of Mexico City and concludes with his return from Mexico to Fort Hamilton, New York.

—— Seven letters to his mother, Mrs. Charlotte N. Sargent. June 22, 1845–December 2, 1848. 17 pp.

—— Three letters to his parents, Mrs. Charlotte N. and Levi Sargent. October 10, 1846–September 20, 1848. 6 pp.

[S–508; B791]

26 BUCHANAN, THOMAS ELY

Eighteen letters to his wife. New York, New York, and San Francisco, California, April 20, 1853–October 15, 1854.

84 pp. 22–27 cm.

A detailed description of the voyage from New York to San Francisco by way of Panama and his work in the office of the port surveyor at San Francisco, with some material on Lola Montez who was a fellow passenger on the latter half of the journey, and a visit to Mariano Vallejo.

[S–684]

27 CALAVERAS, CALIFORNIA. MINERS

A petition to the State Legislature of California. Calaveras, California, March 3, 1853.

1 p. 72½ x 20 cm.

Petition signed by forty-four miners requesting that the State Legislature of California amend and alter its laws for the protection of the miners.

[S–672; C1251]

28 CALIFORNIA (PROVINCE) GOVERNOR, 1782–1790 (FAGES)

"Extracto de la revista de inspeccion executada por mi el coronel Dn Pedro Fages, Governador . . . Peninsula de Californias . . . Rl. Pres. de Sn Francisco 12 Mayo de 1791." Monterey, [California], May 26, 1791."

4 pp. 30½ cm.

Fages' report of his inspection of the presidio at San Francisco commends Argüello, the commander for good discipline and training but recommends that new weapons in larger quantities should be supplied.

[S–756; C1271]

29 CALIFORNIA (PROVINCE) GOVERNOR, 1782–1790 (FAGES)

"Presidiales de la peninsula de Californias. Cavalleria. R¹ presidio de Sn. Diego." Monterey, California, August 27, 1788.

4 pp. 30 cm.

A detailed report on the presidio at San Diego giving the number of soldiers on duty, horses and mules available, and a record of the military supplies on hand. Fages commends First Lieutenant Josef de Quiñaga, in command at the post, and Second Lieutenant Pablo Grijalva on the performance of their duties.

[S–674; C1271]

30 CALIFORNIA (PROVINCE) GOVERNOR, 1782–1790 (FAGES)

"Presid[s] de la Peninsula de Californias. Cavalleria. R[l] Presidio de Monterey." Monterey, California, April 6, 1791.

3 pp. 29½ cm.

Copy of a statistical report on the Monterey presidio outlining the responsibilities of the lieutenant in charge, mentioning that it was his duty to inspect and report on the San Francisco presidio, and giving the number and condition of the officers, troops, horses, mules, and military supplies at Monterey.

[S–753; C1271]

31 CALIFORNIA (PROVINCE) GOVERNOR, 1782–1790 (FAGES)

"Repuestas que satisfazen los reparos producidos por el ayud[te] inspector Don Nicolás Soler en las notas del extracto de la revista que ultimamente ha pasado a la compañia del Pres[o] de Sta Barbara." Monterey, California, August 22, 1788.

8 pp. 29½ cm.

Accompanied by: "Extracto de la revista de inspeccion, que de orden del teniente coron[l] Dn. Pedro Fages, Governor y Command[te] insp[or] de dha peninsula (quien lo forma) executo el ayudante insp[or] D[n] Nicolás Soler a la compania de dho presidio desde 15 de Enero, hasta 4 de Mayo de referido año."

3 pp. 29½ cm.

Soler's report on the Santa Barbara presidio found the garrison adequately clothed and trained in horsemanship but poorly disciplined and badly armed. In his commentary, Governor Fages emphasizes the additional supplies and personnel necessary if the requirements for this presidio, set down in the *Reglamento* of 1781, are to be fulfilled.

[S–673; C1271]

32 CALIFORNIA (PROVINCE) GOVERNOR, 1822–1825 (ARGÜELLO)

Oath of allegiance to Emperor Iturbide. Monterey, California, April 2, 1823.

3 pp. 30½ cm. With typescript.

Signed by the secretary, Haro, six members of the first California legislature, and the governor, Luis Argüello.

Iturbide was crowned emperor of Mexico on July 21, 1822, but communication was so slow that this oath of allegiance by the California officials was not signed until two weeks after he abdicated, March 19, 1823.

[S–630]

33 CALIFORNIA (PROVINCE) GOVERNOR, 1847–1849 (MASON)

A document appointing Walter Colton as Alcalde for Monterey. Monterey, California, September 15, 1847.

1 p. 25 cm.

Signed by R. B. Mason, colonel of the 1st Regiment of U.S. Dragoons and governor of California. The stationery is stamped with the embossed seal of the Headquarters, 1st Dragoons.

[S–511; C128]

34 CALIFORNIA (PROVINCE) GOVERNOR, 1849–1850 (RILEY)

A document signed by Bennet Riley, governor of California, appointing Charles Moore as notary public for the district of San Francisco. The document is addressed to H. W. Halleck, secretary of the Province of California. Monterey, California, October 4, 1849.

1 p. 32 cm.

[S–513; C128]

35 CALIFORNIA. GOVERNOR, 1851–1852 (McDOUGAL)

Letter to Brevet Brigadier General Ethan Allen Hitchcock. San Francisco, California, December 7, 1851.

2 pp., Docketed. 27½ cm.

A request by Governor McDougal that General Hitchcock help supply the forces under Colonel J. C. Hays with equipment in an attempt to put down a reported Indian uprising in the southern portion of the state.

[S–698; C130]

36 CALIFORNIA. LEGISLATURE. ASSEMBLY

Anonymous draft of an address to the California Assembly [1855?].

11 pp. 32 cm.

This address gives the author's opinion regarding the restriction of Chinese immigration into California, favors a plan excluding from the mines those persons who could not obtain United States citizenship, and also provides background information on the entire question of Chinese immigration.

[S–777; C131]

37 CALIFORNIA. LEGISLATURE. ASSEMBLY

Select Committee to whom was referred Assembly Bills 206, 207, 208.

Draft of the report of the Committee to the House [March 7, 1855].

10 pp. 32½ cm.

The Select Committee was formed to consider three bills introduced during the sixth session of the Legislature that were designed to keep the Chinese from the mines. The report of the committee, the final copy of which is printed in the *Appendix to the Assembly Journal, 6th Session, 1855,* is a substitute for the three bills, and proposes to withdraw the privilege of mining from those people unable, by law, to obtain United States citizenship.

[S–778; C1315]

38 CALIFORNIA ANTI-COOLIE ORGANIZATION

Letter to the President and Members of the Six Chinese Companies. San Francisco, California, [n.d.].

2 pp. 26½ cm.

Written by the president of the California Anti-Coolie Organization in reply to a communication in the *San Francisco Call,* the letter warns the Six Chinese Companies of violence and death to those who oppose the organization.

[S–781; C132]

39 CARDEN, JOSEPH W.

A letter to His Excellency, The President, James Knox Polk. Knoxville, Tennessee, November 7, 1847.

1 p. 25 cm.

A veteran of one campaign in Mexico, and anxious to return there, Carden asks appointment as surgeon in the Tennessee Cavalry, citing numerous letters of recommendation, which presumably accompanied his request. All have disappeared except: ALSUP, GIDEON M. Testimonial to J. W. Carden, character, and medical qualifications. Statesville, Tennessee, September 13, 1847. 1 p. 25 cm.

[S–515; C1784]

40 CARNAHAN, S. W.

Letter to John Ramage. South Fork, California, July 29, 1849.

8 pp. 25 cm.

A general description of day-to-day gold mining operations, with some of the factors involved in the preparation and selection of sites and the quantities of gold one could expect from them. There is also some description of Sacramento, with emphasis on the inflated values of land and property.

[S–683; C214]

41 CARTER, TUNSTILL Q.

A letter to James Knox Polk, President. Cerralvo, Mexico, November 15, 1847.

2 pp. 24 cm.

A private in the army, almost illiterate, requests the President to promote him to the rank of lieutenant. "i wish you to gave me the appointment of Lieutenant i will accept of the appointment very thankfully."

[S–516; C246]

42 CARY, THOMAS G.

"Alta California during the Mexican war, 1846–1848," and "Discovery of gold, 1848." Cambridge, Massachusetts, October 1885.

81 pp. 26 cm. Ascribed to Cary by a note on the title page of the copy of the manuscript in the Library of Congress.

The early history of California, its prob-   the Bear Flag Incident, as well as the be-
lems of annexation, John Frémont and   ginnings of the Gold Rush, are discussed.

[S–623]

43   CARY, THOMAS G.

"The Chinese in California."

34–60 pp. 25 cm.

In defense of the Chinese against the po-   this manuscript, examples of which are
sition taken by Governor Bigler in a   also at Harvard and the Library of Con-
speech to the California legislature, this   gress; the Harvard copy being a part of
essay also includes a brief history of   a five-volume series of essays, and the Li-
Chinese immigration into the United   brary of Congress copy being one of three
States. Cary made several fair copies of   essays.

[S–688; C259]

44   [CARY, THOMAS G.]

"The Committee of Vigilance of 1851."

36 pp. 25 cm.

This is a description and history of the   that Captain Waterman of the *Challenge*
San Francisco Vigilance Committee   had mistreated his crew.
formed in 1851 after the incompetence   This closely parallels an article in the
and dishonesty of the authorized law en-   July 1881 issue of *International Review*,
forcement officials were clearly demon-   and is one of at least three fair copies
strated in the Stuart-Burdue affair, until   made by the author, one now in the Li-
the time when it was necessary for the   brary of Congress and the other a part of
elected government of the city to call   a volume in a five-volume series at Har-
upon the committee to prevent mob ac-   vard University.
tion in the disorders following the report

[S–792; C259]

45   CARY, THOMAS G.

"San Francisco Vigilance Committee of 1856."

91 pp. 25 cm.

In a prefatory statement signed and   Francisco, May 15, 1856," and continues
dated Cambridge, October 1, 1885, Cary   with a description of the development
outlines his relationship with the Com-   and operations of the Committee during
mittee of Vigilance, first as an active mem- the three months of its existence. A final
ber and later as an observer acting on   chapter entitled "Good Effects of the
special duty whenever needed by the   Vigilance Committee, Land Titles—Elec-
Committee. The narrative begins with a   tions" discusses these aspects of the Com-
copy of the "Constitution of the Com-   mittee's work, but is mostly a refutation
mittee of Vigilance, Organized in San   of errors of fact in General Sherman's

Memoirs, some of which were corrected in later editions of that work.

This is one of at least three fair manuscript copies made, one being part of a five-volume series at Harvard University, and the other a separate volume in the Library of Congress. Parts of this article parallel one written by Cary for the December 1877 issue of *Atlantic Monthly.*
[S–791; C259]

46 CASTLEMAN, PHILIP F., *b.* 1827

Journal of an overland journey to California, May 2, 1849, to October 27, 1849, and to Oregon in the spring of 1851.

227 pp. 20 cm. With typed transcript.

The journal describes the route from Aetna Furnace, Kentucky, to St. Joseph, Missouri, by way of riverboat, and thence over the Oregon and Applegate trails to California, passing the Big and Little Blue Rivers; the Platte River; Fort Kearney; Castle and Chimney Rocks; Fort Laramie; South Pass; Sublette's, Hudspeth's, and Lassen's cutoffs; to the North Fork of the Feather River; and Sacramento. Part of the Journal parallels that of Samuel McCoy in *Pioneering on the* *Plains,* whom Castleman met and travelled with during the latter part of his journey. After finding little gold, and having been swindled by his employer, Castleman records his journey to Oregon where he began a lumber mill. Staying in Oregon, with one brief journey back to Kentucky, he fought the Indians in the Rogue River War, and became a successful photographer, lumber merchant, and farmer.
[S–745]

47 CHASE, NATHAN

Three letters to his wife. North Fork of the Calavares [*sic*] River, California, March 5, 1852; Angels Camp, California, May 2, 1852; Columbia, California, August 7, 1852.

10 pp. 25½ cm.

Reflection of life on board ship during a voyage to California and of life in the gold fields.
[S–686]

48 CHELTON, JAMES

Letter to his brother and sister. Marysville, California, September 2, 1852.

3 pp. 25 cm.

In this letter Chelton describes the voyage in the bark *Emily* from Panama to San Blas, Mexico, where he transferred to a French ship, from thence to San Francisco, and life in the mines.
[S–682; C419]

49 CHRISTENDORFF, CARL FREDERICH

Journals, January 1, 1859–February 23, 1862; January 1, 1852–October 17, 1863.

2 vols. [i.e., 234 pp.], illus. 18½–19 cm.

Christendorff's journals describe his gold mining activities in and around Oroville, California. They supplement those of his shipmate and friend, Frederich Windeler, in whose diary Christendorff is frequently mentioned. Leaving San Francisco in May 1863, for his home in Kiel, Germany, by way of Panama, New York, and Hamburg, his account covers the voyage and a short period after his arrival home.

[S–749; C4595]

50   CLARK, WILLIAM, 1770–1838

Field notes kept by Captain William Clark, 1803–1805.

67 documents. 25½–104½ cm.

The Lewis and Clark expedition assembled in the winter of 1803 at Camp Dubois, across the Mississippi from the mouth of the Missouri River. The winter was spent in preparation for the long journey to the Pacific which began May 14, 1804. These rough notes, kept by William Clark, second in command of the expedition, cover the period spent at Camp Dubois (December 13, 1803, to May 14, 1804) and the first stage of the journey up the Missouri River to the Mandan Villages, where they spent the following winter (May 14, 1804, to April 3, 1805). The notes, written on scraps of paper of various shapes and sizes, which served as the basis for Clark's more formal journal, were sent back down the river in the spring of 1805 when the expedition resumed its journey. In 1904, when R. G. Thwaites published the journals of the Lewis and Clark expedition, the field notes were not known to be still in existence. They were rediscovered in 1953 in the papers of General John H. Hammond. The field notes were edited by Ernest S. Osgood and published, together with complete facsimiles, by Yale University Press in 1964 under the title, *The Field Notes of Captain William Clark, 1803–1805.*

[S–897]

51   CLAY, HENRY, 1777–1852

A letter to H. R. Robinson thanking him most cordially for the "Lithographic View of the Battle of Buena Vista." Ashland, Virginia, December 24, 1847.

1 p. 26 cm.

Clay expresses his gratitude for the gift of the lithograph, which portrays so well the battle of Buena Vista where his son lost his life.

[S–517; C578]

52   CLAYTON, JOSHUA E.

Correspondence and papers, 1855–61.

50 pp. 25–32 cm.

The correspondence deals mainly with Frémont's Mariposa estate and California geology, Clayton being a mining engineer of some prominence in California.

In addition to miscellaneous deeds and statements of account, the following are included:

—— Copy of a letter to W. A. Eliason. November 21, 1855. 2 pp.

—— Copy of a letter to Joseph E. Palmer. October 26, 1856. 1 p.

—— Copy of a letter to Palmer. October 27, 1856. 3 pp.

—— "Statement of the indebtedness of Frémont & Lockwood for tools, provisions, labor and teams contracted since the 17th day of November 1856 to date, (January 16th 1857)." 3 pp.

—— Draft of an article submitted to the *Mariposa Democrat.* April 5, 1857. 3 pp.

—— Draft of a letter to W. B. Ewer. January 9, 1858. 4 pp.

—— Draft of an article *Mining Interests of California.* January 8, 1858. 2 pp.

—— Draft of a letter to the editor of the *Mariposa Democrat.* March 22, 1858. 3 pp.

—— Draft of a letter to the editor of the *Mariposa Democrat.* July 26, 1858. 4 pp.

—— Draft of a letter to the Honorable S. A. Merritt. January 18, 1859. 2 pp.

—— Copy of a letter to the editor of the *Mariposa Democrat.* [n.d.] 3 pp.

[S–685; C579]

53 CLEMENT, CHARLES S.

A letter written to a friend, Sarah E. Johnston. Camp Bergora, Mexico, October 5, 1847.

3 pp. 25 cm.

Army life as seen through the eyes of an enlisted man in the 1st Massachusetts Volunteers. Although he had not yet seen any fighting, Clement gives a detailed account of marches and countermarches from Matamoros to Monterey and Vera Cruz.

[S–518; C–591]

54 CLUTTER, GEORGE W.

A letter to his wife, Mrs. Sarah M. Clutter. Mier, Mexico, October 5, 1847.

3 pp. 25 cm.

A soldier who enjoys army life relates some individual skirmishes the men in his company had with the Mexicans.

[S–519; C629]

55 COAHUILA AND TEXAS (STATE) GOBERNADOR, 1824–1826 (GONZALES)

"Gobernacion del Estado de Coahuyla y Tejas." Saltillo, Mexico, Decembre 6, 1824.

24 pp. 31 cm.

In this report to an unidentified superior, Governor Rafael Gonzales describes carefully the individual areas of the government under his supervision: the national militia, mail, health, charity, missions, industries, highways, agriculture, and the Indians.

[S–598; C6313]

56 COLLINS, JOHN A.

Letter to Adeline Burgess. San Francisco, California, August 10, 1851.

4 pp. 25 cm.

Collins describes the climate of San Francisco, the agricultural potential of California, and expresses hope for transcontinental railroads and a telegraph system.

[S–696; C694]

57 COLNETT, JAMES, 1755?–1806

Letter addressed "Dear Sir" [Secretary of the British Admiralty]. [n.p., July 5, 1789].

3 pp. 24 cm.

Colnett, in command of a vessel owned by the British South Sea Company, attempted to establish a trading post at Nootka Sound. His arrest and the seizure of his ship brought Britain and Spain to the verge of war. After nine months detention in Mexico, Colnett was released by the viceroy, Revilla-Gigedo. This letter informs the Admiralty of his imminent release and gives his own version of the incidents at Nootka.

[S–617]

58 "CONSIDERACIONES GENERALES SOBRE LA EXTENSION Y EL ASPECTO FISICO DEL REYNO DE NUEVA ESPAÑA." MEXICO CITY, MEXICO, 1806.

90 pp. 29½ cm.

Apparently projected as an exhaustive treatise on New Spain, only the first five chapters have survived. Book I, whose caption has been used in the absence of a general title page, describes the geography of Mexico. Book II is devoted to population and quotes figures taken from the census of 1793. The work includes information on Texas, Arizona, and New Mexico.

[S–664]

59 COOK, J. M.

A letter to his cousin, William H. Leevis. Vera Cruz, Mexico, October 12, 1847.

3 pp. 25 cm.

Cook, a soldier from Georgia, describes his trip from Mier to Vera Cruz and his new surroundings, and comments on army life.

[S–520; C–772]

60 COOMBS, FREDERICK, 1803–1874

Letter to Senator Morgan. Newark, New Jersey, May 22, 1866.

2 pp. 25½ cm.

The noted eccentric writes to Senator Morgan—on the verso of a broadside advertising his temperance lectures—asking for reimbursement of losses caused when his property was consumed by San Francisco fires three times in one year. He supports his claim by mentioning some of his varied philanthropic endeavors.

[S–784; C781]

61 COOPER, MARK A.

A confidential letter written to "Mr. President" [Polk]. Madison Morgan County, Georgia, March 6, 1847.

1 p. 26 cm.

A former congressman urges commissions in the new forces being raised for the war for two of his neighbors on the grounds of military service in the Seminole War and political services in Polk's election.

[S–521; C786]

62 [COPPINGER, JOHN], 1812?–1851?

Draft of a plea for clemency. Yerba Buena, California, November 12, 1846.

5 pp. 31 cm.

Arrested, apparently as a result of his too vigorous complaints against the commandeering of his horses and cattle by Frémont forces, Coppinger writes a plea for clemency, probably to the Alcalde of Yerba Buena, Washington A. Bartlett. Included is a draft of the forwarding letter written by his lawyer giving some of the legal arguments pertaining to the case.

[S–695; C795]

63 CRABB, JAMES

A letter to Henry H. Keeling. Buena Vista, Mexico, July 14, 1846.

2 pp. 25 cm.

Crabb, a member of Company B, 4th Regiment of Louisiana Volunteers (New Orleans), is now located near Matamoras, but in a few days will go to Monterrey where he expects there will be heavy fighting with the Mexicans. He says General Taylor has 15,000 men under his command, and "the volunteers will fight like tigers to sea [sic] the Stars & Stripes wave upon the walls of Mexico."

[S–503; C840]

64 CROSSMAN, GEORGE H.

A letter to General Henry Alexander Scammell Dearborn. Philadelphia, Pennsylvania, November 21, 1847.

4 pp. 11 cm.

A detailed account, written by a staff officer, of Zachary Taylor's preparations for a march on San Luis Potosí, the frustration of his plans by the War Department's transfer of his troops to reinforce Scott, and the alleged political motives for these actions.

[S–523; C884]

65 CROW, ALBION T.

A letter addressed to B. C. St. Cyr. Camp Taylor, Mexico, March 3, 1847.

3 pp. 10 cm. "Army Express" written at the bottom of the address.

A description of the Mexican wounded encountered by the advancing Americans after the battle of Buena Vista.

[S–524; C884]

66 CURTIS, SAMUEL RYAN, 1805–1866

Correspondence of Samuel Ryan Curtis, 1844–1847.

63 letters. 229 pp. 25–32 cm.

Before the Mexican War, Curtis was chief engineer for the Muskingum River project and, at the same time, maintained a law office in Wooster, Ohio. Curtis, Colonel of the 3d Regiment of the Ohio Volunteers, writes his wife almost daily letters which give an excellent historical and personal account of the Mexican War. He relates troop movements in great detail, gives accounts of battles (especially Buena Vista), and concludes with the prospects of returning home via New Orleans. Also included are a few letters addressed to other military leaders.

Other letters and papers for the Civil War period are in the Coe Collection at Yale University.

—— Fifty-five letters to his wife, Belinda Curtis. May 20, 1846–July 20, 1847. 220 pp.

—— Six letters to Major Tompkins. June 6, 1846–June 13, 1846. 7 pp.

—— Letter to General Wool. June 6, 1846. 1 p.

[S–525; C946]

67 CUSHING, CALEB, 1800–1879

A letter written to "My dear Sir" [Nathaniel Niles]. Buena Vista, Mexico, July 20, 1847.

4 pp. 10 cm.

Brigadier General Caleb Cushing, stationed in Buena Vista, writes to Nathaniel Niles concerning affairs in Mexico in general, the feeling of the people toward General Taylor and President Polk, and the possibility of peace negotiations with the Mexican government.

[S–526; C952]

68 DAVIS, GEORGE W.

Letter to Walters [sic] L. Watkins. Secret City, California, December 6, 1850.

4 pp. 25 cm.

Davis gives advice on the best routes for crossing the Country, with some helpful information on conditions to be found, and brings some previously published information up to date.

[S–694; D294]

69 DAVIS, JEFFERSON, 1808–1889

A letter addressed to Lieutenant McNutt, Ordnance Department. [Brazos, Texas, August 20, 1846].

1 p. 10 cm.

On ordnance supplies for the 1st Mississippi Volunteers, which Davis commanded.

[S–527; D294]

70 DENVER, FRANK

Letter to his brother, James William Denver. Sacramento, California, January 19, 1859.

10 pp. 25 cm.

Contains an estimate of the political situation in California and a business proposal. James Denver was at this time Commissioner of Indian Affairs and a prominent figure in the Democratic Party. His brother discusses the possibility of his securing the governorship of California and the presidential nomination. The business portion suggests that the brothers attempt to secure the Placerville—Salt Lake City mail contract should the present holder, George Chorpenning, forfeit it.

[S–693; D437]

71 DENVER, MARY C.

A letter from Mary C. Denver to her brother James William Denver. [n.p.], Mexico, October 6, 1847.

4 pp. 25 cm.

Chiding her brother, then at Vera Cruz with the army, for being a poor correspondent, Mary's letter is primarily concerned with news of local interest to him. The city of Denver was named in his honor some years later.

[S–528; D439]

72 DERBY, GEORGE HORATIO, 1823–1861

Original pen and ink sketches. San Francisco, California? 185–?

5 sketches. 25–25½ cm.

"Oh where, tell me where is Doctor Hitchcock gone?" 20 × 25½ cm. With positive photostat. 21½ × 28 cm.

"Standard Bearer." 19½ × 25 cm.

"Duel between Lieuts. Bell and Williams." 19½ × 25 cm.

"How can ye sing, ye little birds? (hic)"—Burns. 19½ × 25 cm.

"Last appearance of Pottawottomee Brown, Dec –2, 1859." 19½ × 25 cm.

Supposedly from the estate of Dr. Hitchcock's daughter who was Derby's life-
long friend, these sketches lampoon
characters and incidents of San Francisco life in the 1850s.

[S–236; D444]

73 DIX, JOHN ADAMS, 1798–1879

A confidential letter written to General Wool, U.S. Army. Washington,
D.C., April 3, 1847.

4 pp. 25 cm.

Senator Dix congratulates Wool and
Taylor on the victory at Buena Vista and
discusses American military policy and
probable Mexican strategy.
    Accompanied by a fair copy in another
hand.

[S–529; D643]

74 DIXON, G.

Letter to "My dear Parents." San Francisco, California, August 5, 1860.

4 pp. 32½ cm.

Dixon writes primarily about the climate
and the agricultural possibilities he
found in California, mentioning the
rush to the Washoe gold and silver
mines, his living conditions in and
around San Francisco, and the prices of
voyages to California.

[S–783; D645]

75 DOWNEY, JOSEPH T., 1820–

"Odds and ends; or, incidents of a cruise in the Pacific in the U.S. ship
Portsmouth, from January 1845 until May 48, by Fore Peak."

1 leaf, 143, 96 pp. 32½ cm.

Downey gives a delightful and vividly
detailed account of ship life aboard the
sloop of war U.S.S. Portsmouth, as well
as relating the naval conquest of California. Downey used the pseudonyms
"Fore Peak" and "Filings," undoubtedly
hoping to publish his diary at some later
date.
    This manuscript was edited by
Howard Lamar and published by Yale
University Library, 1958, with the title
*The Cruise of the Portsmouth, 1845–
1847;* it was reissued in 1963 by Yale
University Press.

[S–246]

76 DOYLE, SIMON and JAMES

18 letters by James and Simon Doyle to various members of their family. Various places, September 18, 1846, to September 20, 1848.

57 pp. 24–31½ cm. With typescript.

Simon and James Doyle of Rushville,
Illinois, enlisted in the 1st Illinois Volunteers in June 1846. The regiment was
mustered out the following spring and
the brothers enlisted in the Schuyler
Rangers, an independent cavalry troop

attached to General Wool's command. The letters, mostly written by Simon, describe the life and hardships of the volunteers and the various towns in Texas and Mexico where they were stationed.

Journals and letters of the Doyles during the California gold rush in the Coe Collection at Yale University.

DOYLE, JAMES. Letter addressed to Edward Doyle. September 18, 1846. 4 pp.

—— Letter to Simon Doyle. February 17, 1847. 4 pp.

DOYLE, SIMON. Letter to Edward Doyle. May 23, 1847. 2 pp.

—— Letter to Edward Doyle. June 2, 1847. 3 pp.

—— Letter to Edward Doyle. June 9, 1847. 2 pp.

—— Letter to Edward Doyle. July 6, 1847. 4 pp.

—— Letter to Edward Doyle. July 17, 1847. 4 pp.

—— Letter to Miss Margaret Doyle. August 6, 1847. 4 pp.

—— Letter to Edward Doyle. August 13, 1847. 3 pp.

—— Letter to Edward Doyle. October 6, 1847. 3 pp.

—— Letter to James Doyle. October 13 [1847]. 4 pp.

—— Letter to Edward Doyle. November 10, 1847. 3 pp.

—— Letter to Edward Doyle. November 26, 1847. 3 pp.

—— Letter to Miss Margaret Doyle. January 1, 1848. 2 pp.

—— Letter to "Dear Sister." February 19, 1848. 4 pp.

—— Letter to Miss Margaret Doyle. March 15, 1848. 4 pp.

—— Letter to Edward Doyle. August 4, 1848. 2 pp.

—— Letter to Edward Doyle. September 20, 1848. 2 pp.

[S–625]

77 DUPONT, SAMUEL FRANCIS, 1803–1865

Two letters written to R. L. Browning, a lieutenant in the Navy. Wilmington, Delaware, March 6 [1845] and August 24, 1846.

4 pp. 27 cm.

Mostly concerning the U.S.S. *Congress,* of which Browning was First Lieutenant, and to which DuPont was assigned as a member of Commodore Stockton's staff for operations in California waters.

[S–509; D9274]

78 EARLY, JUBAL ANDERSON, 1816–1894

Letter to Major W. W. S. Bliss, Adjutant General of General Taylor's army. Monterrey, Mexico, June 4, 1847.

1 p. 27 cm.

On administrative matters, a pending court-martial, discharges for disabled men, etc.

[S–506; Ea76]

79 EATON, AMOS BEEBE, 1806–1877

Letterbook of Commissary Agent, Amos B. Eaton, 1846–1847.

252 pp. 26 cm. Original binding.

Captain Eaton was Commissary of Subsistence for General Taylor's army. His letterbook contains copies of official letters from November 25, 1846, to July 26, 1847 relating to provisioning the army.

[S–543]

80   ENO, HENRY, *b.* 1798

Correspondence, 1848–1871.

135 pp. 19½–31½ cm.

Henry Eno went to California in 1849 and spent the next twenty years in vain attempts to amass a fortune. He alternated mining with the practice of law, being for several years a judge in Alpine County, California. The correspondence is devoted to mining in California and Nevada, politics, the Vigilance Committee, and business affairs. Most of the letters are from Henry to his brother William in New York, but a few to William from another brother, Edward, are included.

―――― Forty letters to William Eno. December 31, 1848–February 3, 1871. 122 pp.

ENO, EDWARD. Three letters to William Eno. October 7, 1849–August 19, 1867. 6 pp.

WINCHESTER, JONAS. Letter to William Eno, January 10, 1868. 3 pp.

SAWYER, E. D. Letter to William Eno, August 15, 1870. 3 pp.

[S–692; En64]

81   ESQUIVAL, DIEGO

A deposition brought against Colonel Price and his troops when they were in the town of La Cañada in the Territory of New Mexico, County of Santa Fé, New Mexico, May 17, 1847.

3 pp. 31 cm.

Diego Esquival, a clerk in the house of Manuel Alvarez, claims that the troops under Colonel Sterling Price forced their way into the house and plundered it with a resulting loss amounting to "seven hundred and thirty four dollars and sixty five and one half cents and I could not protect the said property."

[S–530; Es69]

82   EYMER, WENCESLAS

Two letters about the missionary work among the Tarahumara Indians. Papigochi, Mexico, February 2, 1696, to August 2, 1707.

2 pp. 31 cm.

Two early manuscripts, one in Latin and one in Spanish, probably addressed to his superior, in which Father Eymer tells what he hopes to accomplish in the mission and the handicaps it is under due to lack of sufficient funds.

[S–657]

Informacion de los PP.es Missioneros
de la Prov.a de Sonora, como se
hallan, al acabar esta visita
del año 1744.

1.º Hallase en Mobas el P.e Buenaventura de Echevar-
ria; como ya noticiè. No me consta, q.e sepa, ò no sepa
aquella lengua, pero mas me inclino à q.e no la sepa
por ser dificil, ni haver estado el P.e La primera vez p.r
mucho tiempo, ni tengo razon de presumir en el P.e
La extraordinaria aplicacion, precisa para aprenderla.
Dho P.e, à mi parecer, no es para Missiones; ha tenido
cuentos pesados active y passive, y luego q.e bolbio à
Mobas, han retoñado algunos con poca edificacion. El
nimio apego àl cuydado de su credito, q.e su P.a piensa
ser muy entero, y en la comun persuassion, es muy cor-
to, y casi incapaz de soldarlo, me haze rezelar, q.e el S.r
no le ha de dar, ni consuelo, ni sossiego. Sta sido notado
de inconstante, y quando pide alguna cosa, vehementissi-
mo en instar; es poco aplicado à la enseñanza de los hijos
y de su boca oì unas proposiciones, q.e solo se pueden
escusar, con tenerlo por leso en el juizio. Se ha reparado
en el P.e mezquindad en algunos Lances, y prodigalidad
en el natural voraz, q.e todos saben y notan. Fuera caridad para los hijos, y mirar para el poco credito del P.e
retirarlo à un Coll.o, en donde fueran estos defectos de menor desedificacion. La falta de Sugetos, y los cuentos pas-
sados, me detuvieron à hazerlo, pero juzgo coram Domino
q.e se debiera hazer.

Mi amantissº Hº in Chrº Juan de Ytor beroaga
P. Chrº &c:

Fino y agradero à mi Hº la remiβion de la carta
no del P. Vanhame, a quien no conozco, Lino del Pe
Miguel Ychabel, que por orden del Pe Pe Prº en
corabao. Agora supliro à mi Hº muy encarecidamen
te, me aga caridad de remitirle la respuesta al Pe
Pe de la Vera Cruf, a quien dhº Pe escribió y Ledió
en las manos la ocaβion, para nuestra corresspondencia.
Puede ser que ayga en el almacen unas tres o dos
libras de Vaynilla: Me la pide el Padre, y yo la
aviβiera Embiar, y no ay forma βino por via
de mi Hermano, a quien suplico, βi hubiera forma
βe la despache al Pe Pe de la Vera Cruf, encargandole
βu despacho con la carta adjunta. Lo que costan mi
Hº la pagará de mi limosna, y βi alguna cosa me embiara
dhº Pe Miguel, recurro à la caridad de mi Hº, rogandole
mucho me lo despache. En lo que mi Hº me conbeiβ diβo
no tengo que deβir, βino que en todo y portodo estoy muy
contento. Diosº lo gde. a mi Hº muchos años: y nose
olbide demi en sus βtas oraciºs. Capigochi y Agº 2 de
1707
                                                De mi Hº
                                                muy Herbo in gmº
Yo, Ce el nombre del Pe Pe de la Vera,
Cruf, por lo qual suplico a mi Hº   Wenceslao Eymer
βirba de ponerle el βobreβrito.

2. MS. No. 82   Wenceslas Eymer

83 EYMER, WENCESLAS

Letter addressed to Father Juan de Yturberoaga, Provincial General of the Society of Jesus. Papigochi, Mexico, May 13, 1707.

1 p. 31 cm.

Reporting the conditions of the mission at Papigochi, which was in the Tarahumara country (now Ciudad Guerrero, Chihuahua), and thanking Father Yturberoaga for funds to carry on the work of the mission.

[S–653]

84 FAULLIN, T. P.

Letter to President James K. Polk. Russellville, Kentucky, April 2, 1847.

1 p. 25 cm.

An office seeker asks President Polk to give him a post in the Far West.

[S–531; F273]

85 FLAGG, JOSIAH FOSTER, 1828–

Journal of a voyage to San Francisco by way of Cape Horn, May 10, 1849–November 23, 1849.

74 pp., illus. 25 cm. With partial typed transcript.

Describing, in the form of a letter to his father, a voyage on the bark Warwick from Philadelphia to San Francisco, giving detailed descriptions of Rio de Janeiro, Valparaiso, and San Francisco, and of the formation and dissolution of the Pacific Mining and Agricultural Association. Flagg was secretary of the Association and played an important part in the political struggle surrounding its formation and destruction. Laid in is a schedule of the ship's position at various intervals, a sketch of the mountain formations around the harbor at Rio de Janeiro, and a letter to his mother in which he describes his life in the mines and in which he has sketched a "Long Tom" mining device.

[S–708; F597]

86 FOLSOM, JOSEPH LIBBEY, 1817–1855

Four letters and a few papers of Joseph L. Folsom. San Francisco, California, 1849–1852.

17 pp. 12½–33½ cm.

Folsom, a West Point graduate, went to California in 1847 as a Captain in the New York Volunteers (Stevenson's regiment). After the Mexican War, he settled in San Francisco becoming a respected member of the community and the first collector of the port of San Francisco under American rule. Investing privately in real estate, he purchased the Leidesdorff estate. The present town of Folsom in Sacramento county is named in his honor.

—— Original signed will. November 29, 1849. 3 pp.

—— Letter to John W. Geary. March 5, 1850. 2 pp. With Geary's request to William M. Eddy. March 7, 1850. 1 p.

—— Notice to Clement S. Humphrey. May 18, 1852. 1 p.

ROGERS, D. Letter to Folsom. October 29, 1840. 2 pp.

SHERWOOD, JOHN. Letter to Folsom. January 19, 1851. 3 pp.

Folsom's bills for laundry et al. April 2 to May 13, 1852. 3 pp.

Property deed signed by David W. Hunt and Folsom. May 12, 1851. 2 pp.

[S–238; F731]

87 FREEMAN, WILLIAM G.

A letter written to Colonel John Munroe. Headquarters of the Army, West Point, New York, July 28, 1849.

3 pp. 26 cm.

Freeman, as Assistant Adjutant-General, sends instructions to the commander of Fort Leavenworth for movement of detachments of the 2d Dragoons and 3d Infantry to Santa Fé to relieve the troops stationed there.

[S–532; F878]

88 FRÉMONT, JOHN CHARLES, 1813–1890

Two letters from John Charles Frémont. November 4 and 5, 1846.

2 pp. 16–21 cm.

—— Letter to Captain John B. Montgomery. November 4, 1846. 1 p.

A letter of instruction to John B. Montgomery to pay W. H. Davis the value of 15,000 percussion caps. Frémont signs himself as "Military Commandant of California."

—— Letter to Quartermaster Snyder. November 5, 1846. 1 p.

Tells Snyder to retain two mules for the wagons.

[S–533; F886]

89 FRIEND, C. W.

Letter to W. L. Coney. Marysville, California, September 22, 1850.

2 pp. 27 cm.

Description of the life of a miner in the gold fields in and around Marysville and the upper reaches of the American River.

[S–691; F916]

90 GAINES, EDMUND PENDLETON, 1777–1849

A letter to Chancellor Kent. Astor House, New York, January 16, 1847.

4 pp. 18 cm.

Gaines, at this time commanding the Eastern Department, sends Kent a copy of a pamphlet on the defense of New York harbor and sets forth his theories on national defense.

[S–534; G128]

91 GARDINER, GEORGE A., 1818–1854, *defendant*

Manuscripts and documents relating to the claim of George A. Gardiner for alleged damages and loss of his silver mine in Rio Verde, the State of San Luis Potosí, Mexico.

88 letters and 9 papers. 249 pp. 21–35 cm. Typescripts of some of the documents.

George A. Gardiner, a practicing dentist and physician in Rio Verde, Mexico, was forced suddenly along with other U.S. residents to leave the vicinity because the troops in the Mexican War were marching toward the area. Gardiner, who had unsuccessfully done a little mining on the side, was clever; he seized this opportunity to press a claim for damages for a nonexistent silver mine, which he claimed was destroyed by the Mexican army. He went to great lengths to obtain documents with supposed official signatures. In boasting that he had won his case on false pretenses, the conversation ultimately came to the attention of our minister to Mexico, Robert Letcher, who ordered an investigation. It was lengthy, but Gardiner was finally convicted and consequently committed suicide.

Some of the documents appeared in a report made by a Special Committee of the House of Representatives, 32d Congress, 2d Session.

[S–544]

92 GARNETT, ROBERT SELDEN, 1819–1861

A detailed letter concerning Buena Vista written to "My dear L." Agua Nueva, Mexico, March 2, 1847.

16 pp. 26 cm.

Robert Garnett, as aide-de-camp to General Taylor, gives a full and detailed account of the events leading up to the battle of Buena Vista.

[S–535; G186]

93 GEARY, JOHN WHITE, 1819–1873

Correspondence, military orders, muster rolls, and a few family letters and papers of John W. Geary during his service in the Mexican War, 1846–1848.

112 letters and papers. 696 pp. 7–53 cm.

John White Geary was both soldier and politician. As politician, he served as Territorial Governor of Kansas 1856–1857; his official papers, in the W. R. Coe Collection, and his business letters and papers for this period, are at Yale University.

At the outbreak of the Mexican War, Geary was Captain of the American Highlanders, which were attached to the "Cambria Legion." He and his company joined the 2d Regiment of the Pennsylvania Volunteers and were sent to Vera Cruz where Geary participated in Scott's advance to Mexico City. Colonel Roberts, the commander of the Regiment, was in such bad health that his responsibilities were left primarily to Geary. After leading the attack at Chapultepec, Geary was placed in command and remained there until the end of the war.

The letters to Geary from his wife, Margaret, and brother, Edward, give an excellent insight into the political thinking of the day on a national level. Captain Samuel H. Montgomery, a brother officer, had been sending letters back to Pennsylvania from Mexico in which he discredited the commander of the 2d Regiment of Pennsylvania Volunteers, Colonel Roberts, and the officers under him—especially Geary. As these letters appeared in the *Pennsylvania Argus,* which was printed in Geary's home town of Greensburg, Pennsylvania, Geary's wife and brother were able to convey vividly public sentiment and reaction to the letters.

These papers also include a number of courts martial proceedings and sentences. None are of special note except the charges preferred against Captain Samuel H. Montgomery by Geary. Other interesting records are the general military orders and the reports which list the names of many of the men who deserted, were wounded, or killed in Geary's regiment.

—— Draft of a political speech in support of Lewis Cass. [n.d.] Unsigned. 5 pp.

—— Copy of a letter to General George Gibson. July 20, 1847. Unsigned. 1 p.

—— Letter to Captain J. Hooker. January 31, 1848. 2 pp.

—— Charges and specifications preferred against Captain Samuel H. Montgomery, Assistant Quartermaster, U.S. Army. December 29, 1847. Signed by eight witnesses. 3 pp. With copy. 2 pp.

—— Copy of a letter to Major General Winfield Scott. October 31, 1847. Unsigned. 1 p.

—— Letter to His Excellency Francis Rawn Shunk. December 10, 1846. 1 p.

—— Copy of a letter to Daniel Sturgeon. 1847. Unsigned. 2 pp.

—— Letter to Major General Worth. October 29, 1847. 1 p.

—— Copy of a letter to Major General Worth. [n.d.] Unsigned. 2 pp.

—— Copy of a letter to George C. K. Zahm. [n.d.] Unsigned. 3 pp.

—— Report of the battle of Chapultepec to Lieutenant Lovell. September 15, 1847. 9 pp.

—— Copy of a letter for a plan for the consolidation of the 2d Regiment, Pennsylvania Volunteers. January 20, 1848. Unsigned. 1 p.

—— Address delivered to the soldiers of his regiment before its discharge from the Mexican War in 1848. Unsigned. 5 pp. With typescript. 3 pp.

—— Anecdote of Santa Anna. [n.d.] Unsigned. 2 pp.

—— Draft of a speech on behalf of the "Cambria Volunteers." [n.d.] 1 p.

ARMSTRONG, I. L. Letter to Geary. December 13, 1848. 1 p.

ARMSTRONG, JAMES. Letter to Geary. September 14, 1847. 1 p.

BIBB, TITUS P. ATTICUS. Certification that Geary served on the military commission. May 13, 1848. 1 p.

BLACK, SAMUEL. Letter to Geary. March 15, 1847. 3 pp.

—— Letter to Colonel Childs, Military Governor of Jalapa. May 25, 1847. 1 p.

BLACK, SAMUEL W. Copy of a letter to His Excellency James K. Polk. February 5, 1848. 1 p.

BOWMAN, GEORGE W. Letter to Geary. January 13, 1848. 1 p.

—— Letter to Geary. February 14, 1848. 2 pp.

—— Letter to Geary. April 12, 1848. 1 p.

BRINDLE, WILLIAM. Letter to Geary. November 14, 1848. 1 p.

BROWATTAN, E., & CO. Letter to Geary. January 25, 1848. 1 p.

CASKEY, ROBERT. Letter to Geary. November 24, 1848. 1 p.

CONRAD, JAMES M. Letter to Geary. November 29, 1848. 1 p.

CRESSWELL, JOHN. Letter to Geary. December 29, 1846. 1 p.

DANIELS, JOSEPH. Letter to Geary. October 28, 1847. 1 p.

DAVIS, GEORGE T. M. Letter to Colonel Roberts. May 13, 1847. 1 p.

DONOUGH, ANDREW. Letter to Geary. January 1, 1848. 1 p.

DUTTON, BENJAMIN F. Letter to Geary. August 3, 1848. 1 p.

EVERHART, E. V. Letter to Geary. March 1847. 4 pp.

FAIRFIELD, JOHN W. Contract drawn up for chartering the ship *General Veazie.* January 12, 1847. Signed by Thomas B. Eastland. 4 pp.

FORSTER, W. Letter to Geary. September 2, 1848. 1 p.

FRICK, CLARENCE H. Letter to Geary. December 13, 1847. 1 p.

——— Letter to Colonel Roberts. April 8, 1847. 1 p.

GEARY, EDWARD R. Sixteen letters to his brother, John W. Geary. December 28, 1846–November 16, 1848. 50 pp.

GEARY, MARGARET A. Six letters to her husband, John W. Geary. April 8, 1847–May 22, 1848 [n.d.] 16 pp.

GIBSON, GEORGE. Letter to Geary. December 4, 1847. 1 p.

GRAVES, R. L. Letter to Assistant Joseph Daniels. October 28, 1847. Signature only. 1 p.

GUTHRIE, JOHN B. Letter to Geary. June 16, 1848. 2 pp.

HACKER BROTHER AND COMPANY. Two letters to Geary. August 4, October 11, 1848. 2 pp.

HAGNER, PETER. Letter to Geary. March 6, 1848. 1 p.

HAMBRIGHT, HENRY A. Letter to Geary concerning the battle of Chapultepec. September 14, 1847. 3 pp.

HARE, NICHOLAS. Letter to Geary. July 13, 1848. 1 p.

HEISTAND, I. D. Letter to Geary. January 11, 1847. 1 p.

HENRY, WILLIAM. Letter to Geary. July 8, 1848. 2 pp.

HEYER, CHARLES H. Letter to Geary concerning the wounded at Chapultepec. September 15, 1847. 1 p.

HUMPHREYS, JOHN. Letter to Geary. October 2, 1848. 2 pp.

IRVINE, ANDREW. Letter to Geary. January 18, 1848. 2 pp.

JACKSON, R. M. S. Letter to Geary. December 18, 1848. 1 p.

JONES, ROGER. Letter to Lieutenant John Keeffe. February 14, 1848. 2 pp.

KLOTZ, ROBERT. Letter to Geary. September 5, 1848. 1 p.

LITZINGER, CHARLES. Letter to Geary. May 25, 1848. 2 pp.

LOESER, THOMAS S. Form letter filled in to Geary. September 5, 1848. 1 p.

LOGAN, DAVID. Letter to his brother-in-law, J. W. Geary. March 20, 1848. 4 pp.

LOGAN, WILLIAM W. Five letters to his brother-in-law, J. W. Geary. January 8–June 8 [n.d.] 14 pp.

McDERMIT, JAMES. Letter to Geary. May 20, 1848. 1 p.

McFARLAND, GEORGE R. Letter to Geary. May 14, 1848. 3 pp.

McGOWAN, GEORGE. Letter to Geary. May 21, 1848. 1 p.

MACKALL, WILLIAM W. Letter written to Geary for General Worth. November 2, 1847. 1 p.

——— Letter to Geary. November 15, 1847. 1 p.

McKAMEY, ALEXANDER. Letter to Geary. November 8, 1847. 1 p.

McNAMARA, ROBERT. Letter to Geary. June 5, 1848. 1 p.

McWILLIAMS, PETER H. Two letters to Geary. March 15, April 4, 1848. 4 pp.

MADSON, JOSEPH L. Three letters to Geary. October 5, November 8, November 22, 1848. 3 pp.

MILLER, F. W. Letter to Colonel Roberts. May 22, 1847. 1 p.

MONTGOMERY, SAMUEL H. Letter to Geary. December 30, 1846. 1 p.

MOORHEAD, J. K. Letter to Geary. December 12, 1848. 1 p.

O'NEILL, J. C. Letter to Geary. December 14, 1848. 1 p.

PATTERSON, ROBERT. Letter to Geary. March 15, 1848. 1 p.

PEARCE, JOHN C. Letter to Geary. December 29, 1846. 1 p.

PENNSYLVANIA INFANTRY. 2d Regiment, 1847–1848. Lists of votes polled in the election for a colonel, lieutenant colonel, and major for the Regiment. November 2–5, 1847. 30 pp.

PENNSYLVANIA INFANTRY. 2d Regiment, 1847–1848. Testimonial that Captain Montgomery's statement, which was printed in the paper about the Regiment, was false. December 9, 1847. Signed by the officers of the Regiment. 3 pp.

PORTER, ROBERT. Letter to Geary. February 27, 1848. 1 p.

POTTS, JAMES. Letter to Geary. May 30, 1848. 2 pp.

REED, ROBERT H. Letter to Geary. November 14, 1848. 1 p.

STIFLEY, JOHN. Letter to Geary. October 1848. 1 p.

THOMAS, LORENZO. Copy of a letter to Major O. Cross. May 17, 1848. 1 p.

TODD, ANDREW. Letter to Geary. September 5, 1848. 2 pp.

WILLIAMS, EDWARD C. Letter to Geary about the battle of Chapultepec. September 14, 1847. 1 p.

WILSON, S. S. Letter to Geary. May 5, 1847. 1 p.

[S–585]

94 GEARY, JOHN WHITE, 1819–1873

Letter addressed to Major General Persifor Smith. Fort Leavenworth, Kansas Territory, September 19, 1856.

4 pp. 25 cm. With typescript.

Geary, newly appointed governor of the territory, assures Smith that he will make every effort to drive out all disorderly bands and try to establish a permanent peace. To accomplish this he needs four or five companies of troops dispatched immediately. (The 1850s were a period of conflict between pro- and antislavery forces in Kansas.)

Other official correspondence of John W. Geary is in the W. R. Coe collection at Yale University.

[S–218; G262]

95 GIDDINGS, JAMES M.

A deposition concerning the plundering of goods in the house of Manuel Alvarez. County of Santa Fé, New Mexico, July 20, 1847.

3 pp. 25 cm.

In the conquest of Santa Fé during the Mexican War, a merchant named Manuel Alvarez claimed his property was damaged by Colonel Price's troops. Giddings felt that Alvarez was friendly to the American cause and if his complaint were valid, it should be investigated.

[S–537; G361]

96 GLASS, ALEXANDER

A letter to "His Excelency [sic] James K. Polk President of the U. States." Leesburg, Tennessee, February 7, 1848.

1 p. 31 cm.

A request for a commission as a 2d lieutenant in one of the new regiments to be raised for the Mexican War.

[S–538; G464]

97 GORDON, BETSEY

Letter to her father. San Francisco, California, February 28, 1854.

4 pp. 23½ cm.

She describes her journey to California by way of Nicaragua, which began with a voyage on the *Star of the West*. She travels by mule back and lake steamer over the Isthmus, and by the steamer *Pacific* to San Francisco. In San Francisco, she begins housekeeping with her husband, and describes the city and living conditions.

[S–726; G653]

98 GORMAN, WILLIS A.

A letter addressed to the Honorable John W. Davis, Speaker of the House of Representatives. Bloomington, Indiana, May 27, 1846.

1 p. 32 cm. With address.

Anxious to join the army, Gorman asks for "some position that will be respectable," and reports that he is raising a company of volunteers. He eventually became Major of the 3d Indiana Volunteers and was wounded at Buena Vista.

[S–539; G681]

99 GRAHAM, ALEXANDER F.

Letter to "Dear Barbour." Council Bluffs, Nebraska Territory, May 19, 1850.

2 pp. 25 cm.

Describing conditions found on the trail; telling of the formation of the Council Bluffs Company under Captain Bemis.

[S–707; G759]

100 GRAYSON, JOHN B.

A letter to George Gibson, Commissary General of the Subsistence Department, giving the prices of food supplies in Mexico. Mexico City, October 16, 1847.

1 p. 21 cm.

A report on his accounts and papers telling particularly about the cost of food supplies in Mexico; the daily ration for the men was thirty-two cents.

[S–540; G796]

101 GREER, ALLEN

Agreement between Allen Greer, Asa Greer, and Henry B. Curtis for the Greers "to depart on an adventure to California for the purpous [*sic*] of gaining, by working in the placers or gold mines of that region. Mount Vernon, Ohio, March 2, 1850.

3 pp., docketed. 27 cm. With typed transcript.

By the terms of this agreement, Allen and Asa were to go to Oregon or California, whichever proved more profitable, for a period of two working seasons, to prospect and mine for gold or to pursue any other endeavor that would produce a profit. Henry B. Curtis was to be a partner by investing a sum equal to the others, but was to receive, after the initial investment was returned, a smaller share of the profits.

[S–706; G86]

102 GUAJARDO, LUIS ALBERTO, 1862–1940, *compiler*

"Apuntes datos y noticias para la historia de Coahuila." Primarily Piedras Negras, Mexico, [1613–1911].

Ca. 5,300 pp. 8½–35 cm. Typewritten transcripts, with some handwritten marginal notes.

Luis Alberto Guajardo, a brigadier general in the Mexican army, collected transcripts taken from the official archives of Monclova, Saltillo, and Santa Rosa, the latter now known as Muzquiz, Coahuila, probably as source material for a projected history of Coahuila.

These documents are more extensive than the title would indicate, for not only do they give the history of Coahuila, but also the history of the Mexican nation itself. A few of the topics included are: the history of the presidio of Santa Rosa; El Capitan Don Juan de Ugalde; the official visit of Tueros, governor of Monclova; the controversy between Viceroy Flores and Ramón Castro concerning the repairs of the moat of the presidio of Santa Rosa del Sacramento; capture of the first insurgents of 1810, and their downfall in Bajan, Coahuila, as reported by Gregorio De La Concepcion; the ancient mines in Coahuila; the wars of independence of 1810, (written by a friend of Hidalgo's), and 1821; Iturbide; recognition of Mexican Independence by Great Britain; the cholera epidemics of 1833 and 1849; the campaign into Texas in 1836; and the revolutions of 1910 and 1911.

[S–668]

103 HACKELTON, SAMUEL, *d.* 1848

A letter to George W. Chace. Santa Fé, New Mexico, February 1, 1848.

4 pp. 25 cm.

A description of his trip over the Santa Fé Trail to join the 1st Illinois Volunteers at
Santa Fé.   [S–569; H115]

104 HANDERSTEIN

Letter to his wife, Harriet, and his children. Fort Laramie on the Platte,
June 24, 1849.

2 pp. 25 cm.

Tells of life and sickness met on the trail, the necessity of selling his wagon for lighter equipment, and of his plan to accompany soldiers through the Sierra Nevada Mountains to California or Oregon and then to San Francisco by sea.

[S–705; H192]

105 HARDIE, JAMES ALLEN, 1823–1876

Letter to the San Francisco Town Council. San Francisco, California,
November 10, 1847.

2 pp., docketed. 25 cm.

Major Hardie, commanding the Northern Military District, requests the Town Council to provide a place of confinement for prisoners of the town, because he has found it necessary to withdraw most of the military guard from the town to the presidio.

[S–703; H219]

106 HASKIN, JOSEPH A.

A letter to Roger Jones, Adjutant General. Fort Brown, Texas, May 23,
1846.

1 p. 25 cm.

Requesting a pardon for, and giving the details connected with, a deserter, Patrick
Dalanay.   [S–542; H273]

107 HERRIET, H. S.

A letter to his wife, Electa. Sacramento, California, June 5, 1851.

12 pp. 25 cm. With typescript.

Herriet gives an excellent description of his voyage to California with interesting comments on life in general on the coast during the gold-rush days.

[S–618]

108 JALAPA, MEXICO (CITY)

Official correspondence and papers. Jalapa, Mexico, 1847–1848.

243 pp. 17–32½ cm.

A collection of letters describing the problems which beset the city of Jalapa when it was occupied by the Americans after the battle of Cerro Gordo. Thomas

Childs, as its first military governor, permitted the Ayuntamiento to carry on its own government with few exceptions; he was succeeded by George Wurtz Hughes for the remainder of the occupation.

Some of the difficulties concerned the activities of the guerrillas in towns around Jalapa and on the highways, care of the wounded American soldiers, pillaging of livestock, election of new alcaldes, and the ultimate readjustment for continuing local affairs after the American troops were withdrawn from the city.

BANDERILLA, MEXICO. Juzgado. Letter to the "Gefe Politico del Departmento de Jalapa." April 26, 1847. 2 pp.

BANKHEAD, CHARLES. Letter to the First Alcalde of the Ayuntamiento. October 26, 1847. 2 pp.

BESANCON, LORENZO A. Letter to the Alcalde. February 24, 1848. 1 p.

CASTRO, FRANCISCO DE P. Letter to the Alcalde of Jalapa. May 8, 1847. 3 pp.

JALAPA, MEXICO (CITY) ALCALDE. Ten letters to the Ayuntamiento and the military governor (Childs). October 19 to November 11, 1847. 18 pp.

JALAPA, MEXICO (CITY). Ayuntamiento. Letter to "Gen. en Gefe de las fuersas de los Estados Unidos del Norte." April 26, 1847. 4 pp.

——— Five letters to the governor of the state (Soto). April 16 to June 11, 1847. 13 pp.

——— Three letters to the military governor (Childs). April 22 to June 10, 1847. 7 pp.

——— Twenty-nine letters written to the military governor (Hughes). October 1847 to May 29, 1848. 63 pp.

——— Proceedings and letters to various members of the Ayuntamiento including the alcaldes, the treasurer, Juan Franco, and the interpreter, Leonardo Perez. April 22 to June 18, 1847. 17 pp.

——— Letter to the Alcalde at Naolinco, Mexico. January 11, 1848. 2 pp.

JALAPA, MEXICO (CITY). Juzgado. Fourteen letters to the Ayuntamiento by members of the council and the secretary, Joaquin Guevara. October 28, 1847 to January 25, 1848. 17 pp.

——— Orden numero 127 de General en Gefe. May 1, 1847. 3 pp.

JALAPA, MEXICO (CITY). Military governor, 1847 (Childs). Six letters to the alcaldes and the town council. April 27 to June 10, 1847. 9 pp.

——— Letter to "Gobernador del Estado," (Soto). June 8, 1847. 2 pp.

JALAPA, MEXICO (CITY) Military governernor, 1847–1848 (Hughes). Seven letters to the alcaldes and the town council. November 1 to December 1847. 15 pp.

JALAPA, MEXICO (DEPARTMENT). Letter to "Gen. en Gefe de las fuersas de los Estados Unidos del Norte." April 18, 1847. 2 pp.

——— Twenty letters to the Ayuntamiento. March 31, 1847 to May 27, 1848. 42 pp.

KENNEDY, DIEGO. Letter to "Y Ayuntamiento de esta Ciudad." December 26, 1847. 3 pp.

MARIN, TOMAS. Letter to the governor of the state (Soto). November 22, 1847. With plea dated December 1847. 2 pp.

NAOLINCO, MEXICO. Juzgado. Two letters to the Alcalde of Jalapa. April 29, 1847 to January 10, 1848. 4 pp.

PEREZ, LEONARDO. Letter to Juan Carr. May 25, 1848. Copy. 4 pp.

——— Letter to Joaquin Guevara, secretary of the Ayuntamiento. February 29, 1847. 1 p.

POLANCO, FRANCISCO. Letter to Guevara. June 15, 1847. 2 pp.

ROA, JOSÉ MARÍA. Letter to the Ayuntamiento. December 14, 1847. 1 p.

SANTA ANNA, ANTONIO LÓPEZ DE, 1795–

1876. Letter to the governor of the state of Vera Cruz (Soto), April 14, 1847. Including draft of Soto's reply. April 15, 1847. 3 pp.

U.S. ARMY. Army of Mexico, 1845–1848. Letter to José M. Ochoa and the Ayuntamiento. February 21, 1848. 1 p.

VERA CRUZ, MEXICO (STATE) Gobernador, 1847 (Soto). Two letters to the Ayuntamiento and the "Sr. Alcalde 1° Presidente del Y Ayuntamiento. June 12 and 13, 1847. 5 pp.

[S–588]

109 JESUITS. MEXICO

List of missions and missionary heads in the Southwest. [n.p.], *ca.* 1740.

11 pp. 21½ cm.

Missions which were established in California, Northern Mexico, and Pimería Alta.

[S–632]

110 JESUITS. MEXICO

List of missions of the Tepehuana and Topia Indians. Durango, Mexico, 1750.

2 pp. 21 cm.

Giving routes and distances.

[S–638]

111 JOHNSON, JOHN A.

Journal of an overland journey to California, March 5–August 24, 1849.

130 pp. 16 x 9½ cm.

A detailed account of Johnson's overland journey to California with the Fort Stephenson Mining Association. Relying primarily on the Oregon Trail, the company used the Sublette Cutoff, left the trail at the Raft River, and continued by way of the Humboldt River and Sink. Described are many of the landmarks, life on the trail, the value of mules on the trail as compared to oxen, and the eventual breaking up of the company, which emphasizes the difficulties of keeping a company together. A less detailed account of the journey home by way of Panama and New Orleans completes the journal. Laid in is a copy of the constitution of the Fort Stephenson Mining Association clipped from the *Lower Sandusky Freeman*.

[S–710]

112 JONES, CADWALLADER

A letter addressed to His Excellency, The President of the U.S. Hillsboro, North Carolina, November 4, 1847.

1 p. 27 cm.

A petition in behalf of John Cameron who wished to apply for the vacancy in the North Carolina Regiment as Quartermaster. The regiment was to leave soon for the Mexican War.

[S–546; H273]

113 KEARNY, PHILIP, 1814–1862

Letter to Thomas S. Jesup. New York, New York, September 12, 1848.

2 pp. 25 cm.

Letter written by Philip Kearny, Captain of the 1st Dragoons, to Quartermaster General Thomas S. Jesup, justifying the expenses which he incurred while raising a full troop of dragoons.

[S–548; K215]

114 KING, CLARENCE, 1842–1901

Letter to Professor J. E. Clayton. 18 Wall Street, New York, New York, December 2, 1885.

2 pp. 20 cm. With addressed envelope.

Making inquiries about the Hot Creek Mining District in Utah.

[S–747; K58]

115 KING, F. M.

Letter to William Allen. Port Byron, New York, February 1, 1849.

1 p. 25 cm.

Inquiry into the rates for life insurance for the California miners and those enroute, including questions regarding the differences in cost of insuring lives of those travelling over certain specified routes.

[S–704; K581]

116 KING, JAMES STUART

Correspondence, 1852–1853.

29 pp., 1 illus. 19½–28 cm.

Correspondence primarily with his parents and brothers, including some from acquaintances and business associates. King went to the mines to make his fortune, and failing that, looked for other means of support. A letter from a friend tells about Colonel William Walker of filibustering fame, and makes several references to his "surveying expedition" to Lower California. Giving advice to his younger brother, King describes the hardships encountered and the small chance for success in California. His descriptions of the country include some mention, with an illustration, of bull fighting in San Diego. The remainder of the correspondence concerns his brother John who accompanied him to California but who was more inclined to wander than work in spite of several offers, mostly from Quartermaster Department officers.

[S–702; K582]

117 KING, JOHN NEVIN

Journal of an overland journey from Illinois to California, April 27, 1850–August 27, 1850.

16 pp. 31½ cm.

Journal of his overland journey to California in which he describes the route from Erin Bank, near Berlin, Illinois, by riverboat to St. Joseph, and thence by Alexander and Hall's passenger train via forts Leavenworth and Kearney, over the Oregon Trail and Sublette's Cutoff past Fort Hall to the Raft River, down the Humboldt River, and finally to Sacramento, with notes on the weather conditions, availability of food and water, ferrying, firewood, and road conditions along the way. A letter to his father tells of his accepting a position with the Quartermaster Department at Benicia.

[S–723; K5825]

118 KING, JOSEPH CRAWFORD

Letter to George F. Andrews. San Francisco, California, August 31, 1849.

2 pp., docketed, with address. 25 cm. With typed transcript.

As a result of a lack of success in the mines, the crowded conditions in the fields, and the rough work involved, King considers obtaining other employment.

[S–701; K583]

119 KING, THOMAS STARR, 1824–1864

Letters and miscellaneous papers of T. S. King. Boston, Massachusetts, San Francisco, California, et al., 1854–1864.

45 pp. 18–20 cm.

King, a Massachusetts minister, moved to San Francisco in 1858 to become the pastor of the Unitarian church. King's correspondence shows him a staunch supporter of the Union cause during the Civil War.

—— Ten letters to W. R. Alger. Boston et al., 1854–1864. 45 pp. 18–20½ cm.

—— Letter to Mr. and Mrs. Corey. Boston, 1850. 1 p. 18½ cm.

—— Letter to W. G. Bryan. Boston, 1857. 2 pp. 20½ cm.

—— Brief autobiographical sketch. Boston, 1852. 1 p. 25½ cm. Unsigned. On verso, statement that this was written at the request of the editor of *Hundred Boston Orators.*

—— Letter addressed to Chairman of Lecture Committee of "M. L. Association." San Francisco, March 4, 1861.

[S–255; K587]

120 KIP, WILLIAM INGRAHAM, 1811–1893, *bishop*

Letter to Alexander Wells. San Francisco, California, May 8, 1854.

1 p., docketed. 20 cm.

Bishop Kip asks Wells to give any legal assistance that the Reverend Dr. Clark may need in securing a charter for Trinity College in San José.

[S–787; K628]

121 KNOWLTON, CYRUS D.

Letter to his parents. Placerville, California, January 22, 1854.

4 pp. 25 cm.

The gold mines are closed down because of unusually cold weather and a lack of water; an acquaintance is brutally murdered.

[S–700; K765]

122 LACKEY, ALBERT

Journal, December 5, 1849, to June 26, 1850.

3 vols. [i.e., 270 pp.]. 20½ cm.

Journal of a voyage to San Francisco by way of Cape Horn and Juan Fernandez from Salem, Massachusetts. Albert Lackey was a school principal from Salem, who sailed with his wife and two children for California by way of Cape Horn as members of the Salem Mechanics Mining and Trading Association. He gives detailed descriptions of the voyage, including the crowded conditions on the ship, the activities of the passengers during the long journey, and the handling of the ship by the crew and officers. His position as president of the company enables him to provide authoritative information on the way the mismanagement of the affairs of the company by the agent hindered the progress of the ship and endangered the welfare of the passengers. Laid in is a newspaper clipping listing the members of the company.

[S–796]

123 LASUÉN, FERMIN FRANCISCO, *d.* 1803

Letter addressed to Fray Francisco Palou. Mission of Santa Barbara, California, December 13, 1787.

4 pp. 21 cm.

A plea from Lasuén, Superior of the Franciscans in California, to Francisco Palou, second president of the California missions, to stop the sea-otter hunting, as the time and effort involved could be more advantageously employed in promoting the welfare of California.

[S–752; L356]

124 LATTURE, JACOB

Letter written to his brother and sister but addressed to his cousin, Samuel Akard. National Bridge, Mexico, March 14, 1848.

3 pp. 31 cm.

Life and illnesses common to army life as told by a soldier to his family.

[S–549; L357]

125 LEGGETT, AARON

Letter addressed to Governor [*sic*] Marcy (Secretary of War). New York, October 16, 1845.

4 pp. 25 cm.

An American merchant, with business connections in Mexico, informs the Secretary of War of an alleged plot of the British and French to isolate California from Mexico so that they could set up an independent government in the territory. This would prevent California from ever being annexed to the United States.

[S–550; L524]

126 Letter addressed to Bernardo de Rolandegui. Sonora, Mexico, November 1707.

2 pp. 30½ cm. Author's signature illegible.

The author, in response to a solicitation for help from the mission, is willing to double his gift of cattle. Kappus, a Jesuit, is named as the only reliable one to collect this alms and drive the cattle to the port of embarkation.

[S–660]

127 LEWIS, JABEZ G.

Letter to Isaac Chrisman. Panama City, Panama, April 18, 1849.

3 pp. 31 cm. With address.

Observations of life in Panama City made while awaiting passage to California.

[S–699; L586]

128 [LEWIS, NANCY M. (CURRY)]

Letter to her daughter, Fannie. Sacramento, California, June 26, 1852.

4 pp. 25 cm.

This mother extols the beauty of the country with descriptions of the climate, the bountiful harvests, the ease of travel from the states, and the availability of employment as a dressmaker, as a plea for Fannie and her family to come to California.

[S–730; L588]

129 LOCKWOOD, SAMUEL, 1803–1893

Correspondence and papers including orders, inventory of supplies, and account sheets of Commander Samuel Lockwood, U.S. Navy, 1846–1848.

3 letters, 55 papers and orders. 71 pp. 21–42 cm.

Samuel Lockwood's papers, in addition to lists of supplies and account sheets, contain orders concerning naval maneuvers of the Home Squadron while it was stationed near Vera Cruz in the Gulf of Mexico from 1846 to 1848. Among the orders are those of David Conner and Matthew C. Perry as Commodores of the Home Squadron, which was composed of a sizable number of small craft.

[S–560; L814]

130 LOPEZ, RAMON

Letters addressed to Father Juan Rivas, director of the missions, viceroys Pedro Garibay and Juan Ruiz Apodaca, and José Darío Argüello, governor of Baja California. Loreto, California, December 23, 1808, to March 17, 1818.

45 pp. 21–31 cm.

Lopez, president of the Dominican order in California, tells Juan Rivas, the director, about the deplorable condition of the missions; at the same time he informs him of the physical and financial needs for maintaining the missions, concluding with a report on the "Real Presidio de Loreto."

[S–639]

131 McCOY, JOHN, 1816–1914

"Notes of my trip from Independence, Missouri to Santa Fe and Chihuahua, 1848."

40 pp. 18½ cm. With typescript and manuscript articles written later on his early days in Independence.

The government contracted with McCoy and his party to transport supplies to the troops stationed at different Western posts, as well as to purchase goods for the New Mexican and Chihuahua trade. At the same time McCoy agreed with the Litsendorfer Company to freight considerable merchandise for them to Santa Fé. The expedition, with McCoy in charge, left Independence on May 10, 1848; McCoy had returned to Independence by 1849.

Binder's title: *Freighting and trading expedition to Santa Fe.*

The book, *Pioneering on the Plains* written by the four McCoy brothers, Alexander, William, John, and Samuel, contains a chapter, "Along the Santa Fé Trail in 1848," which is a slightly different version of this manuscript. The book was privately printed in 1924.

[S–210]

132 McFARLIN, WILLIAM H.

Letter to his wife, Margaret. [n.p.], January 1, 1852.

37 pp. 12 x 7½ cm.

Writing in a Gregory's Express Letterbook, "designed to facilitate correspondence" between the States and California, McFarlin tells of the results of his mining experiences of the past three years, and those of some of their friends, many of whom did quite well. Having just heard from his wife for the first time since his arrival in California, he asks his wife to join him there, as he would like her help in establishing a boarding house, which, he feels, would be much more profitable than mining. Printed on the letterbook is a description of the services of Gregory's Express Company.

[S–729; M164]

133 MALASPINA, ALESSANDRO, 1754–1809

Letters, documents, and papers pertaining to the Northwest Coast of North America. Various places, 1788–1792.

262 papers. 631 pp. 13½–37 cm.

Quedo como sïpre enteramt. y de corazon subordinado
sugeto, y rendido à los superiores preceptos de V.R.
y ruego à Dios N. S.or gue à V.R. en su Sta Gracia
ms. as. Misn. de Sta Barbara y Dic.e 23 de 1797.

B.L.M. à V.R.
Su Vendido, y mas Ynutil Subdito

Fr. Fermin Fran.co de Lasuen

Saludan à V.R. los Padres de esta Misn. y son
en ella en el dia 677 Christianos, y 4 Catecume-
nos.

Libre comercio de las Nutrias muy perjudicial à
Las Misiones.
Resp.a 6 de Ag.to n.º 4

3.   MS. No. 123   Fermin Francisco Lasvén

Importa que con toda la brevedad compre vmd. en Cadiz un Relox de longitud pa. faltriquera, el mas exacto que vmd. encuentre, surtiendole con quatro, ó cinco vidrios de respeto, por si se rompiese el de su uso; y tambien cinco almanaques nauticos correspond. al año de 1787. y otros tantos pa. el de 1788, que se cree los vendia el librero Pablo Caxis, y de no haverlos los remplasaria vmd. con otros tantos libros del Conocimto. de tiempos de la Acada. de Ciencias de Paris pa. los mismos años.

El Relox deve ~~custodiarse~~ pa. hacer viage custodiarse en bolsa de gamusa, y dentro de un casoncito de Madera bien relleno de algodones y así este, como los diez Almanaques, ó Conocimtos. de tiempos, bien enfardado todo lo pondria vmd. en poder del Capitan Genl. de la Armada à qn. prevengo lo q. deverà practicar, y tambien pa. el pago de todo al Yntendte. de ese Depart; con quien tratarà vmd. al efecto. Prevengolo todo à vmd. no dudando de su celo é inteliga. el mejor y mas breve desempeño. Dios &a. Ma. 16. Dice. de 1785.

Sr. Dn. Alexandro Malaspina.

4. MS. No. 133   Alessandro Malaspina

After exploring the Pacific Ocean near Asia in 1784, Malaspina was eager to organize a scientific expedition on a grandiose scale for the purpose of reaching Kamchatka and the Straits of Anian, connecting the Pacific and the Atlantic oceans, which were supposedly discovered by Ferrer Maldonado in 1588.

By November 1788 Malaspina was ready to present his ideas and a request for two new corvettes to the king of Spain, who readily agreed because Spain was interested in improving her hydrographic maps of the West Coast of the Americas. Although this trip was called a journey around the world, it actually was an exploration of the Pacific Ocean.

Antonio Valdés, the Spanish Minister of Marine, gave Malaspina a free hand in selecting his own scientific staff, his co-commander, José Bustamente y Guerra, and all necessary equipment; in supervising the construction of two new corvettes, the *Descubierta* and the *Atrevida;* and in collecting scientific reference books, which had to be obtained from London and Paris.

Sailing from Cadiz, Spain, July 30, 1789, and proceeding along the west coast of Africa, the expedition crossed the Atlantic near the equator to Montevideo in South America, continued southward to the Falkland Islands, rounded Cape Horn and, sailing north along the west coast of South America, arrived at Acapulco, Mexico, in May 1791. Here it was necessary to replace the two painters as they were too ill to continue, and Revilla-Gigedo, the Mexican viceroy, appointed Tomás Suría to take their place.

The manuscripts do not take us any further than Acapulco, but the expedition went as far north as Yakutat Bay, and, not discovering the northwest passage, retraced its course along the West Coast of both North and South America, around Cape Horn, and back to Spain.

There are some miscellaneous items among the papers: an account of the shipwreck of the *San Pedro Alcantara* off the Portuguese coast in 1786, written by the ship's captain, Manuel de Eguia, to Antonio Valdés, Spanish Minister of Marine, who had befriended Malaspina; extracts and map from Laperouse's voyage to the China Sea in 1785–1788; and a fine hand-colored map, apparently the coast of Ecuador, Panama, Salvador, and Guatemala, dated 1790. Felipe Bauza, who was in charge of charts and maps on this voyage, may have drawn this map.

MALASPINA, ALESSANDRO. Fifty letters and reports to Antonio Valdés. February 21, 1786, to December 3, 1790. 146 pp.

ALCALA-GALIANO, DIONISIO. Letter to Valdés. June 29, 1791. 1 p.

BERMUDES, JOSEPH. Letter to Valdés. February 3, 1789. 1 p.

BUSTAMENTE Y GUERRA, JOSÉ. Letter to Valdés. February 2, 1791. 1 p.

CENERE, JUAN BAPTISTA. Letter to Alberto de Sesma. June 13, 1789. 1 p.

CORDOVA, LUIS DE. Eleven letters to Valdés. February 10, 1786, to August 21, 1789. 24 pp.

CORONADO, SALVADOR XIMENEZ. Letter to Conde de Florida Blanca. March 19, 1791. 6 pp.

EGUIA, MANUEL DE. Letter to Luis de Cordova. February 7, 1786. 2 pp.

ESPINOSA Y TELLO, JOSÉ. Letter to Valdés. January 19, 1789. 2 pp.

FERNAN-NUÑEZ, CARLOS JOSÉ GUTIERREZ DE LOS RÍOS Y ROHAN CHABOT, 6th CONDE DE. Thirteen letters to Valdés. March 19, 1786, to April 9, 1789. 23 pp.

—— Report. March 23, 1786. 1 p.

GARCHITORNEA, LEON DE. Letter to Intendente General de Marina. April 21, 1789. 3 pp.

[GIL Y SERNOS, FRANCISCO?]. Letter to Valdés. May 20, 1790. 1 p.

GUTIERREZ DE RUBALCAVA, JOAQUIN. Ten

letters to Valdés. December 16, 1788, to September 29, 1789. 31 pp.

LaTorre, Luis de. Two letters to Cordova. February 13 and 14, 1786. 2 pp.

Llaguno, Eugenio. Two letters to "Junta Suprema de Estado." November 13, 1788, to July 20, 1789. 4 pp.

Mazarredo, Joseph. Five letters to Valdés. December 13, 1788, to October 16, 1789. 20 pp.

Mendoza y Rios, Josef de. Letter to Valdés. June 20, 1790. 3 pp.

Muñoz, Xavier. Three letters to Valdés. May 26, 1786, to May 30, 1786. 6 pp.

Navarrete, Martins Fernandez de, 1765–1844. Letter to Valdés. February 2, 1792. 4 pp.

Olavides, Martin José, Conde de. Two letters to "Mi tío y Sor Marques de Aranda." February 27–July 15, 1790. 19 pp.

Orozcoz, Josef. Two letters to Valdés. December 13, 1789. With an unsigned reply in the left margin dated March 20, 1790. 5 pp.

Peña, Josef de la. Letter to "Señor Comandante del Rio de la Plata." February 19, 1790. 9 pp.

Piñeda, Antonio. Three letters and lists. September 17, 1790–1792. 6 pp.

Porlien, Antonio. Letter to Valdés. February 5, 1789. 2 pp.

Revilla-Gigedo, Juan Vicente Güemes Pacheco de Padílla Horcasitas y Aguayo, Conde de. Eleven letters to Valdés. August 27, 1790–December 30, 1791. 34 pp.

Romero y Landa, José. Letter to Valdés. December 17, 1788. 1 p.

Sesma, Fermin. Five letters and report to Valdés. December 19, 1788–August 28, 1789, and [n.d.]. 11 pp.

Sevena, Pedro de. Three letters to Valdés. April 20, 1789–June 5, 1789. 7 pp.

Tejada, Felix de. Letter to Valdés. December 20, 1788. 1 p.

[Valdés y Bazan, Antonio]. Nine letters to Carlos José Gutierrez de los Ríos y Rohan Chabot, 6th Conde de Fernán-Nuñez. March 24, 1786–April 22, 1789. 14 pp.

—— Twelve letters to Joaquin Gutierrez de Rubalcava. December 9, 1788–August 25, 1789. 13 pp.

—— Eight letters to Cordova. February 21, 1786–August 28, 1789. 11 pp.

—— Twenty-eight letters to Malaspina. December 16, 1785–July 25, 1789. 46 pp.

—— Four letters to Joseph Mazarredo. December 12, 1788–August 20, 1789. 6 pp.

—— Two letters to Francisco Xaxier Muñoz. June 23, 1786–June 30, 1786. 3 pp.

—— Letter to Antonio Porlien. January 6, 1789. 2 pp.

—— Letter to José Romero y Landa. December 9, 1788. 2 pp.

—— Five letters to José Fermin. December 12, 1788–August 20, 1789. 5 pp.

—— Three letters to Pedro de Sevena. April 15, 1789–June 10, 1789. 6 pp.

—— Letter to Felix de Tejada. December 9, 1788. 1 p.

—— Letter to José Varela y Ulloa. January 24, 1789. 1 p.

—— Letter to Viceroy [Gil y Sernos] del Peru. January 24, 1789. 2 pp.

—— Letter to Viceroy and Captain General de las Provincias del Rio de la Plata. August 7, 1789. 1 p.

Varela y Ulloa, Josef. Letter to Valdés. August 20, 1789. 1 p.

There are several unidentified letters, extracts from Laperouse's voyage. October 28, 1788. 5 pp.

Report for an unidentified Spanish newspaper. August 18, 1789. 4 pp.

[S–662]

Exmo Sôr

Doy a V.E las mas rendidas gracias por
mi ascenso a Capitan de Fragata, con que
V.E me dexa tan obligado, como deseoso de
hacer los mayores esfuerzos por correspon
der a sus intenciones.

Seguimos en esta Ciudad procurando de-
sempeñar la comision de nro cargo, y el
teniente de Navio Dn Manuel Novales la
curacion de su larga y penosa enfermedad
con alguna mejora: el de Fragta Dr Arcadio
Pineda, que trabaja incesantemente en el ra-
mo que tiene asignado, hace con esta fecha
una representacion a S. M. por manos del
Sôr Capitan general de la Armada por
no haver sido incluso en la promocion.
Suplico a la bondad de V.E no tome à
mal este recuerdo ni menos el que di-
rija su instancia con mi debil apoyo; pu
es lo he hecho por parecerme justa.

Dios que la importante vida de V.E m
à. Mexico 29 de Junio de 1794.

Exmo Sôr

Dionisio Alcalá-Galiano

Exmo Sôr Bô Fr Dn Antonio Valdés.

5.   MS. No. 133   Dionisio Alcalá-Galiano

exâmenes de los ante-
riores de igual especie,
y extractos importantes
al mayor acierto en él.
Por todo lo qual hallo
digna de aprobacion
en todas sus partes la
referida propuesta.

Nuestro señor que á
V.E. mue años, como
deseo. Madrid 13 de
Dic.e de 1788.

Ex.mo S.or

Joseph de Mazarredo.

Ex.mo S.or B.o Fr. Dn Antonio Valdés.

134 MALTHY, MRS. M. J.

Letter, on illustrated lettersheet, to "My dearest Lou." San Francisco, California, April 30, 1854.

2 pp., illus. 27 x 42 cm.

Written on a pictorial lettersheet with a view of San Francisco in 1854 (Peters, *California On Stone,* No. 37), this letter tells about the city's cosmopolitan pop- ulation and some of the entertainment found around the city, including a performance of *Norma* by Madame Bishop.

[S–728]

135 MASSIDA, PEDRO PABLO

History and census of the missions in Pimería Alta. Various places, *ca.* 1740.

6 pp. 31 cm.

[S–651]

136 MATAMORAS, MEXICO. MILITARY GOVERNOR, 1846–1848

Orders: nos. 4, 6, 23, 25, 32, 35 and 94. Matamoras, Mexico, August 4–October 7, 1846.

23 pp. 25–31½ cm. With copies in Spanish: nos. 14 and 94 in Spanish only. Signed: John M. Brannan, 2d Lieutenant, 1st Artillery, Adjutant; by order of Colonel Clarke.

Regulations issued by the American military governor covering such subjects as sale of liquor, possession of firearms, and restriction of movement of the Mexican citizens.

[S–592; M412]

137 MATAMORAS, MEXICO. PREFECT

Announcement made by Jesús Cárdenas, Prefect, to the citizens of Matamoras, Mexico. [n.d.]

1 p. 31½ cm.

The Prefect announces that the American forces will reach the Rio Grande in two days and that local officials and citizens will sally for the defense of the territory.

[S–595; M4121]

138 MAYER, BRANTZ, 1809–1879

"Mexico in 1841 & 1842." New York and Mexico.

360 pp. 25½ cm. With edited typescript.

This journal, written by Brantz Mayer when he was secretary of the U.S. Legation in Mexico, 1841–1842, is "intended rather for myself than others," indicating a personal account. But, there are historical references throughout, especially to the entire Texas question prior to the Mexican War. Mayer returned to the United States in November 1842 and added many newspaper clippings to his diary reflecting the Mexican viewpoint toward the Mexican War, our relations with Mexico on the Texan affair, and the declaration of war against the United States by Mexico. Of special interest is the American effort to secure release of the members of the Texan Santa Fé expedition captured by the Mexicans.

Mayer's book *Mexico As It Was and As It Is* (New York, 1844), was in large part based on this journal.

[S–217]

139 MAYNARD, LUCIUS E.

Letter to his grandfather. Sacramento City, California, September 16, 1849.

3 pp. 24½ cm.

After a discussion of miner's earnings as compared to the wages available in Sacramento, Maynard writes a short narrative of his journey to California by way of Cape Horn.

[S–727; M454]

140 MAZATLAN, MEXICO. MILITARY GOVERNOR, 1847 (HALLECK)

Orders requiring all Mexican military forces to report to headquarters. Mazatlan, Mexico, November 15, 1847.

1 p. 26 cm.

Henry W. Halleck, military governor of Mazatlan, issues orders to all Mexican citizens and those attached to the military forces to report to headquarters at once. Those who do not will be treated as spies.

Text in Spanish.

[S–541; M456]

141 MEEK, B. H.

Letter to "Friend Swett." Nevada [California], August 5, 1851.

3 pp. 25½ cm. With typed transcript.

Giving his absent partner a résumé of recent gold mining activities both at their mine and in neighboring mines.

[S–794; M47]

142 MELLUS, HENRY, 1815?–1860

Two letters to William Appleton and Company. San Diego, California. December 3 and 17, 1844.

3 pp. 28 cm. Addressed.

Reporting on business conditions and his activities as San Diego agent for the company, and including his estimate of the political situation during the revolt of the Californians against General Micheltorena.

[S–776; M489]

143 MERCER, SAMUEL, *d.* 1862

A letter written to Major Munroe about the Mexican attack on vessels in the harbor. U.S. brig *Lawrence,* Brassos de Santiago, Mexico, March 28, 1846.

3 pp. 32 cm.

In his letter to Major Munroe, Commander Mercer of the U.S. brig *Lawrence* says that he has taken the liberty of sending seamen to protect the vessels in the harbor as they are being attacked by the Mexicans.

[S–558; M535]

144 MERRILL, JERUSHA (DEMING) 1815–

Five letters to her brother and sister-in-law, Mr. and Mrs. Selden Deming. San Francisco, California, 1849–1853.

13 pp. 25–28½ cm. With addresses. Typed and manuscript transcripts.

Conditions in San Francisco during early gold-rush times are reflected in these letters to relatives back home in Connecticut. Mrs. Merrill dwells at length on inflated land values, the turmoil and unsettled atmosphere, the high cost of living, and the advantages of investing in real estate and commodities rather than in mining. A letter is included from her husband to her brother requesting information on certain investments made by Jerusha before leaving for California.

[S–789; M552]

145 MEXICAN WAR

Eight articles concerning the Mexican War.

26 pp. 12½ cm.

Eight anonymous articles dealing with President Polk's message on war with Mexico, his prolonging the War, sending General Scott to Mexico to take command, and Congress' appreciation of General Taylor's performance in the War.

[S–552; M574]

146 MEXICAN WAR

Unsigned manuscript articles on the capture of Mexico City. [n.p.], 1847.

22 pp. 38 cm.

An excellent, well-written account of the siege of Mexico City including such chapters as: "The Advance to the Capital," "Santa Anna's Installation as President," "Santa Anna's Dispatch," "Battle of Buena Vista," "Brillant Campaign in New Mexico," "Gen. Taylor and the Presidency," concluding with "Vera Cruz and Castle Taken."

[S–561]

147 MEXICO (VICEROYALTY)

"Instrucciones reservadas que traxeron de España algunos señores Vireyes" signed by Antonio Bonilla, secretary of the viceroyship, Mexico and Spain, 1754–1789.

644 pp. 31 cm.

A collection of instructions issued by King Ferdinand VI to his viceroy, Juan Francisco de Güemes y Horcasitas, Conde de Revilla-Gigedo in Nueva España, together with additional instructions by later viceroys to their successors for administering religious and civil affairs in New Spain.

Later published in: *Instrucciones que los Vireyes de Nueva España dejaron a sus sucesores* . . . (Mexico, 1867).

[S–666]

148 MEXICO (VICEROYALTY) VICEROY, 1612–1621 (CORDOBA)

Letter addressed to the officials of the city of Zacatecas. Mexico City, Mexico, July 8, 1616.

2 pp. 30 cm. With typescript.

On the difficulties and expense of sending two missionaries to New Mexico, and the offer of José Tremiño to aid in this enterprise.

[S–633]

149 MEXICO (VICEROYALTY) VICEROY, 1746–1755 (REVILLA-GIGEDO)

"Autos fechos en virtud de un Superior Despacho Del ex^{mo} Señor Virrey Governador y Capitan Genl Destos Reynos." Mexico City, Mexico, October 13, 1747, to June 27, 1748.

56 pp., map. 31 cm.

Papers and reports relating to an expedition ordered by the Viceroy to reconnoiter the borders of the Rio Grande, re-establish the missions, and establish a presidio at Junta de los Rios (near the present Presidio, Texas). Most of the reports were prepared by Captain Domingo Antonio García, militia captain at San Felipe Real, Chihuahua, who was ordered to furnish the escort. They deal with difficulties in securing men and equipment, misunderstandings between religious and military authorities, etc. The map shows the location of missions and presidios in the general area between El Paso and Junta de los Rios.

[S–612; M5741]

150 MEXICO (VICEROYALTY) VICEROY, 1746–1755 (REVILLA-GIGEDO)

Letter addressed to the Most Reverend Padre, Juan Antonio Balthasar. Mexico City, Mexico, February 22, 1753.

20 pp. 31 cm. With "Dictamen" dated February 15, 1753.

The letter and "Dictamen" relate especially to twenty-two missions that are being transferred from the Society of Jesus to the diocese of Durango. The Viceroy recommends that Balthasar, the Padre Visitador, establish new missions in the Colorado and Gila areas.

[S–611]

151 MEXICO (VICEROYALTY) VICEROY, 1771–1779 (BUCARELI)

Letter addressed to [Francisco Pangua] guardian of San Fernando College. Mexico City, Mexico, January 14, 1776.

1 p. 30 cm.

Bucareli, the Mexican viceroy, appoints José Antonio Nozedal as chaplain for either of the two new missionary settlements in California—San Diego or Monterey.

[S–762; M5743]

152 MEXICO (VICEROYALTY) VICEROY, 1771–1779 (BUCARELI)

Signed letter addressed to Francisco Pangua, guardian of San Fernando College. Mexico City, Mexico, August 16, 1775.

2 pp. 30 cm.

The new chaplains, Ramon de Usson and Vicente de Santa María, are en route to the San Diego and Monterey missions in California, but Bucareli, the Mexican viceroy, feels they are unworthy of this position and requests the Bishop of Guadalajara to replace them.

[S–670; M5743]

153 MEXICO (VICEROYALTY) VICEROY, 1771–1779 (BUCARELI)

Signed letter to the guardian [Francisco Pangua] of San Fernando College. Mexico City, Mexico, December 6, 1775.

3 pp. 30 cm.

Bucareli, the Mexican viceroy, notifies the guardian of San Fernando College that the soldiers and supplies which the missionary fathers had requested are now being sent to California.

[S–671; M5743]

154 MEXICO (VICEROYALTY) VICEROY, 1771–1779 (BUCARELI)

A signed letter to Father Superior [Raphael Verger] of San Fernando College. Mexico City, Mexico, July 7, 1772.

1 p. 30½ cm.

Bucareli, the Mexican viceroy, tells the Father Superior of San Fernando College that he has ordered Barri, governor of California, to transfer the cattle from the old missions to the new ones being established at San Diego, Monterey, and San Francisco.

[S–669; M5743]

155 MEXICO (VICEROYALTY) VICEROY, 1795–1798 (BRANCIFORTE)

Letter addressed to the Father Guardian of the College of Pachuca. Mexico City, Mexico, June 8, 1795.

3 pp. 31 cm.

Transmits a royal order on the method of reimbursement of travel expenses for missionaries bound for California, those returning after completion of their ten-year service, or those sent home as invalids.

[S–646]

156 MEXICO. EJÉRCITO. COURTS-MARTIAL. BARBERO, 1851

Documents and affidavits. Puebla, Mexico, October 28, 1851, to August 20, 1853.

8 pp. 32 cm.

Report of the 1851 trial and acquittal of General Estevan Barbero and his associates for having pronounced in favor of continuing the war with the United States after the armistice had been signed.

[S–607; P9634]

157 MEXICO. EJÉRCITO. EJÉRCITO DEL NORTE

A letter to the first Justice of the Peace of Jiménez. Rancho del Patitl, Mexico, October 7, 1840.

2 pp. 20½ cm. With heading, "Cuerpo de Ejército del Norte." Signed: M. Arista.

Arista asks cooperation from the Justice of the Peace in locating the rebel, Antonio Canales. Between 1838 and 1840 the Federalists, under the leadership of Canales, attempted to set up an independent government in the northeastern states of Mexico bordering on the Rio Grande. They were frequently aided by volunteers from Texas.

[S–600; M57433]

158 MEXICO. EJÉRCITO. EJÉRCITO DEL NORTE

A letter addressed to the Justice of the Peace. Santander, Mexico, October 12, 1840.

1 p. 20½ cm. With heading, "Cuerpo de Ejército del Norte." Signed: M. Arista.

Arista wants the Justice of the Peace to send without delay any information on the movements of the Federalists.

[S–601; M57433]

159 MEXICO. EJÉRCITO. EJÉRCITO DEL NORTE

Two letters from General Mariano Arista to Pedro Garcia. Monterrey, Mexico, August 20 and 22, 1841.

4 pp. 27 cm.

On problems of frontier defense against the Indians and Texans and the effect on them of recent political developments.

[S–605; M57433]

160 MEXICO. JUNTA DE FOMENTO DE CALIFORNIAS

"El ciudadano Bartolome de nacion Irlandes sre permiso para la colonisacion en las Californias introducion porcion de familias Irlandesas y Mexicanas." Mexico City, Mexico, September 27, 1824, to February 10, 1825.

13 pp. 30–31 cm.

Earlier unsuccessful attempts were made by José Figueroa and John Hale to colonize upper California. In 1824 an Irishman, Bartholomew Richards, proposed to establish a colony of Irish and Mexican settlers in the area. His petition, assuring the Mexican government that he would abide by their laws and author-ity, was then sent to the president of the Junta.

Letters on the colonization scheme from Lucas Alaman and Juan Guzman, members of the Foreign Affairs Department, and a letter from Tomás Salgado, member of the Junta, are included.

[S–755; M5744]

161 MEXICO. JUNTA DE FOMENTO DE CALIFORNIAS

"Exposicion hecha a la junta en 26 de Marzo de 1825 por el Sr. Dn Francisco de Paula Tamariz sobre le recuperacion del puerto de la Bodega ocupado por los Rusos; y establecimiento en el mismo de un Puerto Militar—y Plan Politico, Militar para la ocup^{on} de este Puerto," Mexico City, Mexico, 1825 and 1826.

24 pp. 20–30 cm. (16 pp. copies)

The *expediente* contains a report by Francisco de Paula Tamariz to the Junta on the Russians in California together with a detailed political and military plan for their expulsion. Laid in are a copy of a letter from the Minister of Foreign Relations to the Minister of War on the project, and a further report by Tamariz.

[S–667; M5744]

162 MEXICO. JUNTA DE FOMENTO DE CALIFORNIAS

"Junta del Fomento de las Californias. Of^o de exp^{tes} n° 3. f. 3. año de 1824. Expediente de el Extablecimiento de esta Junta—selebro su la sesion el día 2 de Julio de 1824." Mexico City, Mexico, 1824–1825.

82 pp. 20–32 cm.

The Junta de Fomento de Californias was established in Mexico in 1824 for the purpose of promoting settlement and development of Alta and Baja Califor-nia. These letters give a list of the Junta's members and discuss its organization, expenses, and responsibilities, from its beginning until November 1825.

[S–751; M5744]

163 MEXICO. JUNTA DE FOMENTO DE CALIFORNIAS

"Junta del Fomento de las Californias—sobre el informe dado, por el Sᵒʳ Dⁿ Augustín Fernandez de Sⁿ Vicente sobre el estado de las Californias en el año de 1821." Mexico City, Mexico, 1824–1826.

9 pp. 20–30 cm. (5 pp. copies). Signed: Juan Guzman, Manuel Gonzalez de Ibarra, José Ignacio Ormaechea.

The activities of the Russians at Fort Ross were a constant source of worry to the Mexican government, fearful of Russian aggression and the possible loss of California.

The *expediente* contains a report by Agustín Fernandez de San Vicente on the strength and dispositions of the Russians in California, together with letters of transmittal.

[S–675; M5744]

164 MEXICO. JUNTA DE FOMENTO DE CALIFORNIAS

"Ofo de expᵗᵉˢ nᵒ 7. f.7. año de 1825. Reflexiones sre la destinacion mas conducente que se le puede dar al navio de guerra *Asia,* y Bergantin *Constante* hechas en virtud de orn. del exmo. sr. ministro de relaciones por el vocal de esta junta Dn. Francisco de Paula Tamariz." Mexico City, Mexico, June 21, 1825.

14 pp. 21–30 cm.

A rough draft to the Secretary of State by Tamariz, speaker of the Junta, recommending the use of the newly captured Spanish warships, *Asia* and *Constant,* for extending and stimulating the commercial activities between California, Asia, and Manila, and protecting the Mexican interests on the west coast. The ships should be permanently docked at Monterey from which point, sailing north to Bodega Bay, they could drive out the Russians who were encroaching on Mexican interests.

[S–761; M5744]

165 MEXICO. JUNTA DE FOMENTO DE CALIFORNIAS

"Sobre los Decretos del Congreso de los Estados Unidos del Norte en Sbře de [1]824 relativos á la apertura del camino hasta el Nᵛᵉ Mexico etc linea Divosoria y convenio con los Rusos." Mexico City, Mexico, April 11, 1825.

6 pp. 29½ cm. Signed: Francisco de Paula Tamariz.

Drafts of two reports to the Junta on the implications for California of recent actions by the United States Congress in opening the Santa Fé Trail and in concluding a treaty with Russia establishing the boundary between Russian and American territory bordering on the Pacific. The Mexican newspaper *El Sol* for September 22, 1824, which is bound in, contains a translation of the treaty.

[S–754; M5744]

166 MEXICO. LAWS, STATUTES, ETC.

Decree of September 14, 1847, issued by President Santa Anna, providing that for the duration of the war with the United States, the seat of government might be located at any point in the republic. Mexico City, Mexico, 1847.

2 pp. 31½ cm.

Promulgated by José Ramon Pacheco, ministro de Relaciones. Issued the day before Santa Anna abandoned Mexico City, the constitutional seat of government, before the advancing American forces.

[S–604; M5754]

167 MEXICO. PRESIDENTE, 1846 (PAREDES Y ARRILLAGA)

"At the last hour. Manifesto of his excellency the provisional President of the Republic to his fellow citizens." Mexico City, Mexico, March 21, 1846.

4 pp. 32 cm. Signed: Mariano Paredes y Arrillaga.

Contemporary manuscript copy of an English translation of his *Manifesto del Ecsmo. Sr. Presidente Interino de la Republica à sus conciudadanos.* Issued just before the outbreak of war, it is mainly a denunciation of American aggression in the annexation of Texas. It was published, together with supporting documents, under the title *Ultimas communicaciones entre el gobierno Mexicano y el enviado estraordinario y ministro plenipotenciario de los Estados-Unidos, sobre la cuestion de Tejas* (Mexico, 1846).

[S–564; M575]

168 MEXICO. PRESIDENTE, 1847–1848 (LA PEÑA Y PEÑA)

Letter to Señor Don Mariano Riva Palacio. Querétaro, Mexico, February 24, 1848.

2 pp. 27 cm.

Urging Riva Palacio to come to the capital to help in forming a new cabinet.

[S–602]

169 MEXICO. SECRETARÍA DE HACIENDA Y CRÉDITO PUBLICO

Two letters written to the Dean de Santa Iglesia Metropolitana. Mexico City, Mexico, November 20 and 26, 1835.

4 pp. 29½ cm. With heading: Secretaría de Hacienda

In order to equip the troops to be sent to suppress the rebellion in Texas, the Secretary of the Treasury requests the Dean and Chapter of the cathedral to lend the government 40,000 pesos, to be repaid from the first receipts of the treasury. In the second letter the amount is raised to 50,000 pesos to be paid in two installments. As the largest property owner in the country, the Church was usually in better financial condition than the government.

[S–590; M5756]

170 MEXICO. SECRETARÍA DE LA DEFENSA NACIONAL

An official letter to Don Gregorio Gómez signed by Tornel. Mexico City, Mexico, December 2, 1835.

4 pp. 30 cm. With heading: Secretaría de Guerra y Marina.

On behalf of the President, Tornel informs Gómez of his promotion to brigadier general for defeating the Mejía expedition. José Mejía, with the cooperation of certain Texan leaders, had organized an expedition in New Orleans to seize Tampico and raise a revolt. However, his ship was wrecked, his forces were decisively defeated by Gómez, and Mejía fled with a few survivors.

[S–597; M5757]

171 MEXICO. SECRETARÍA DE LA DEFENSA NACIONAL

Letter to General Gabriel Valencia. Hacienda de San Antonio, [Mexico], August 19, 1847.

1 p. 30½ cm. With heading: Ministerio de Guerra y Marina. Signed: Alcorta.

Lino José Alcorta, Minister of War, informs General Valencia that the Americans are preparing to advance on Tacubaya, and that he has ordered General Mora y Villamil, chief of engineers, to conduct a reconnaissance. General Valencia is to assist him with whatever troops he needs. On the following day the Americans not only advanced as predicted, fighting the battle of Contreras, but also overran the village of San Antonio where Alcorta had made his headquarters, and overwhelmed the main Mexican force at Churubusco.

[S–603; M5761]

172 MEXICO. SECRETARÍA DE RELACIONES EXTERIORES

"Trado de paz con los Norte Americanos." Various places, Mexico, August 27 to September 18, 1847.

13 pp. 22–31½ cm.

An interesting group of letters relating to the peace treaty with the United States. They cover the appointment of Atristain, Couto, Herrera, and Mora y Villamil as the Mexican commissioners, progress of the negotiations, and such problems as Mexican prisoners, notably the guerrilla leader Juan C. Rebolledo, held by the Americans.

[S–608; M5758]

173 MEXICO. TREATIES, ETC., 1848 (LA PEÑA Y PEÑA)

"The original manuscript draft of the treaty of armistice . . . ending the Mexican War . . . between the government of Mexico and the general of the U.S. forces preparatory to the actual ratification of the treaty of Guadalupe-Hidalgo." Mexico City, Mexico, February 22, 1848.

16 pp. 27½ cm. With corrections and bound with typescript.

Title from typescript. Text of manuscript begins:

"Reunidos los infrascritos en la ciudad de Mejico a 22 de Febrero en 1848 p^a celebrar el tratado de treguas que esta prevenido en el Art° 2°. del de la paz, firmad en la ciudad de Guadalupe-Hidalgo el dia 2 del presente, y para este efecto, habiendo sido nombrados los dos primeros por el Sup^r Gobierno de los Estados Unidos Mejicanos y los dos siguentes por el Mayor General de los Estados Unidos de America y en Gefe de sus Ejércitos W. O. Butler; despues de Canjeados sus plenos poderes han convenido en los Articulos siguentes."

[S–615]

174 MILLER, WILLIAM W., 1812–1851

Journal of a voyage to California by way of Cape Horn and of life in the gold fields of California. February 10, 1849–December 30, 1850.

183 pp. 38 cm.

Covers shipboard life on the bark *Lanerk* during a voyage to California by way of Cape Horn, the mining of gold in and around the Tuolumne River region of California, and a return voyage as far as the Isthmus. Detailed descriptions of shipboard life, including diversions employed to while away time, and of business transactions with the officers and crew; day to day life of the prospector and miner; a discussion of the value of supplies and food in the mining regions. Included are lists of the members of the Boston Mechanics Mining and Trading Company, the Norfolk and California Mining Company, the Neponset California Mining Company, and the Roxbury and California Mining Company, all of whom were on board the *Lanerk*, along with a roster of the officers, crew, and passengers. Laid in is a list of the ships entering and leaving Rio de Janeiro during the period from February 20 to April 25, 1849. A description of Miller's death while on his way home, signed by Moses Sweetser, ends the journal.

[S–199]

175 MOONEY, P. S.

Twenty-seven letters to his brother. Various places, February 3, 1862–October 2, 1870.

79 pp. 19½–31½ cm.

P. S. Mooney was a farmer in the east who went west to find work, becoming a stage driver and then Marysville Agent for the Oregon Stage Company. The letters contain observations on Oregon and California, particularly the climate, agriculture, prices, postage rates, and routes.

[S–722; M779]

176 [MORRISON?] ROBERT

A letter to his cousin, Miss Eloise P. Morrison. Camp Saltillo, Mexico, February 7, 1847.

6 pp. 31½ cm. Signed: Robert.

Written by a member of the American occupation force at Saltillo, the letter gives the enlisted man's view on army life, his own officers, and the Mexican people. It also contains a detailed description of the capture of Lieutenant Cassius M. Clay and a detachment of Kentucky cavalry by the Mexicans.

[S–562; M834]

177 MOSS, CAROLINE M.

A letter addressed to Captain O. P. Moss. Clay County, Missouri, November 2, 1846.

14 pp. 25½ cm.

A long personal letter from an officer's wife to her husband telling him about incidents and friends at home. Captain Moss, in the 1st Regiment of Missouri Mounted Volunteers, served in the Mexican War under Colonel Doniphan. It is evident from this letter that the two men were personal friends as well.

[S–563; M855]

178 MOXLEY, CHARLES G.

Five letters to his sister, Emily Moxley. Laurel, Prince George County, Maryland, April 14, 1849–February 15, 1850.

16 pp. 25–32½ cm. With addresses.

Beginning his correspondence at St. Louis, Moxley writes of his overland journey to California in 1849, traveling by riverboat to St. Joseph, by mule train to Fort Kearney (now Nebraska City) and Fort Childs (now Fort Kearney), and thence over the Oregon Trail. Upon arrival in California, he tries his hand at mining, but finds his old trade of carpentry more profitable and stable.

[S–712; M873]

179 MOZIÑO SUÁREZ DE FIGUEROA, JOSEPH MARINO, *d.* 1819

"Relacion de la ysla de Mazarredo. . . . " Mexico City, Mexico, 1793.

187 pp. 20½ cm.

Under the command of Bodega y Quadra, Moziño Suárez, a botanist, was attached to the Spanish expedition to Nootka Sound in 1792. His "Relacion" gives an interesting and minute account of the Indian civilization, their social life and customs, construction and adornment of their dwellings, their government, religious beliefs, natural resources, and commerce of the area. The explorations to the northwest coast made by James Colnett, Robert Gray, William Douglas, and John Kendrick, are described, as well as the seizure by the Spanish of the *Argonaut, Princess Royal,* and the Portuguese ship, the *Iphigenia,* concluding with the controversy between the English and Spanish over the seizures.

[S–634]

180 NAYSON, D. W.

Two letters to James Quimby. Panama City, Panama, and Georgetown, California, February 22, 1849 and November 30, 1850.

5 pp. 25 cm.

On his way to California by way of the Isthmus, Nayson pauses to write about the difficulties of the journey in the earlier part of the rush to California. A second letter, of which only a fragment is available, is considerably more critical in its description of the journey, particularly when referring to Panama City itself.

[S–797]

181 NESS, RICHARD, *b.* 1810

Account of an overland journey to the Pacific coast and return by sea by way of Panama. 1848–1849.

65 pp. 15½ × 10 cm.

Recording an overland journey that begins in Brooklyn, passes through Canada to Chicago, and thence to California by way of Council Bluffs and South Pass as a member of the Express Company, and the return to New York by sea via Panama. Ness, an Englishman naturalized in Chicago while en route, dutifully records all his expenses and income, and shows considerable profit after mining in and around the Yuba River region. Returning to New York after a very difficult voyage in which his ship, the bark *Belgrade*, is nearly sunk in a hurricane, he divorces his wife for infidelity and goes back to England. Includes personal memoranda.

[S–709]

182 NYE, GEORGE

Letter to his mother. Horse Shoe Bend, River Merced, California, February 22, 1851.

4 pp. 24½ cm.

A warning that California's climate, quite different from most found in the United States, accounts for the large death rate there. He, however, experienced in traveling to many parts of the world, finds the California climate the best he has ever experienced.

[S–724; N983]

183 NYE, MRS. HELEN

Letters. Various places, 1852–1871.

25 pp. 18–25½ cm.

Letters to her family, mostly to her sister, Mary, from Don Pedro's Bar, California, in which she describes her voyage as far as the Isthmus, and in which is reflected life on the frontier from the woman's point of view as she runs a boarding house, tutors foreign children, and weathers a very destructive flood.

[S–725; N9835]

184 OAXACA, MEXICO (CITY) Junta Patriótica para recaudar los do-
nativos para la guerra de Tejas.

Letter to the governor of the State of Oaxaca. Oaxaca, Mexico, December 13, 1842.

12 pp. 27 cm. With list of contributors. Signed: Manuel J. Bohórquez.

In order to finance the war against the rebellious Texans, the Mexican govern-ment was forced to rely on voluntary contributions. This letter transmits the list of names and amounts contributed from the city of Oaxaca and neighboring districts for November 1842.

[S–593; Oa9]

185 AN "OLD MINER"

Letter to "Mr. Editor." Mariposa, California, January 22, 1856.

6 pp. 32 cm.

Referring to a letter published on Janu-ary 17, 1856 apparently taking issue with the legislature for passing laws barring the Chinese from the mines, the "Old Miner" shows why, in his opinion, such legislation was necessary.

[S–779; Ol2]

186 ORD, EDWARD OTHO CRESAP, 1818–1883

Draft of a report on an expedition to the Santa Cruz Mountains. Monterey, California, February 16, 1848.

4 pp. Docketed. 25 cm.

The expedition was undertaken to investigate reports of horse stealing in the area.
[S–721; Or2]

187 [ORD, EDWARD OTHO CRESAP, 1818–1883]

Incomplete Letter to "My dear." Rio de Janeiro, Brazil, September 16,
1846.

12 pp. 27½ cm. With typed transcript.

An incomplete retained draft of a letter describing part of the voyage of the ship *Lexington* to California to which Ord was assigned with his artillery company. Described in particular are Rio de Ja-neiro, where the ship was required to spend ten days for reprovisioning and re-pairs, shipboard life, and an encounter with a Spanish slaver.

[S–719; Or2]

188 [ORD, EDWARD OTHO CRESAP, 1818–1883]

Incomplete Letter. Monterey, California, November 20, 1847.

3 pp. 25 cm.

Ord, in command of a fort and quarters he had constructed at Monterey, de-scribes life at the fort and in the sur-rounding country. Laid in is General

Relacion de la Ysla de Mazarredo

De su descubrimiento, situacion y producciones naturales: Sobre las constumbres de sus havitantes Gobierno, Ritos, Cronologia, Ydioma Musica, Poesia, Pesca, Caza y Comercio de la Peleteria: Con la relacion de los Viajes hechos por los Europeos especialmente Españoles, y del convenio ajustado entre estos y los Yngleses &, por

D. Joseph Mariano Moziño Suarez de Figueroa Botanico Naturalista de la Real Expedicion de Nueva España y de la de limites al Norte de California Año de 1793.

quien mataba mas; mas reconocido en esa lugar de idolatria que se halle md. flechas
y offrecen y cañutos de tabaco, una faxa &c. llamo los viejos y por medio de un
interprete les dixo quatro razones, las quales oidas instantanea mente ellos mismos
quiçar y pegaron fuego a dhas cabezas, y en su lugar exigieron una Santissima
Cruz. Sentado esto; se infiere claram.te Ser del Seno del Rey nros. que el
Corazon de la Viscaya Reyno bastante en hostilizado como lo enseña la experi-
encia de algunas naciones de Barbaros es el lugar donde estamos y ya ha havido
ocasion en que ayan intentado los enemigos la union con ellos; y asegurar sus
entradas y salidas con mas libertad; que si Dios no huviera permitido les resisti-
essen, no ay duda fuera mucha la affliccion y hostilidad que padeciera la Viscaya
y doblados los gastos que Su Mag.d huviera que reducirles. Y que siquiera se dio-
curren Ser necessario, que el que se quisieren Sus Ministros. Dios nro S.r provea
de lo que fuere maior honrra Suia. Yo quedo muy esperanzado en el zelo
apostolico de V.R.ma como hijo de N. S. P. S. Fran.co que será todo sucesos
en la mejor providencia. Cuia salud &c. Sea muy buena y que D.s nros.
la continue larg.a a g.e consuelo de sus subditos gracias a Su Mag.d quedo bueno deseando acertar en cosa de tanto peso y serv.o de D.s que nos g.e
a V.R.ma m.chos a.s en toda felicidad. S. Fran.co de la Junta Junio 4 de
1715.

Q.mo P. N. Comm. Gen.

B.L.M. de V.R.ma Su menor Hijo y subdito q.e le venera

Gregorio Osorio

Q.mo P. N. Com. Gen.l P. Luis Morote

8.   MS. No. 190   Gregorio Osorio

Order 11, Washington, D.C., October 9, 1933, part of which changes the name of the Gigling Military Reservation, the site of Ord's original fort, to Camp Ord.

[S–720; Or2]

189 [ORTIZ ZAPATA, JUAN]

"Descripcion de la Nueva Viscaia." [n.p., n.d.]

157 pp. 32 cm.

No general title page; title from caption on first leaf.

Consists mainly of Father Zapata's account of his visitation to the missions in 1693, preceded by a general description and history of Nueva Viscaya written by an unknown Jesuit in the late eighteenth century. Nueva Viscaya covered the present states of Durango, Chihuahua, Sinaloa, and Sonora. Considerable space is devoted to the Apache Indians and their depredations; the accounts of the individual missions are detailed.

[S–643]

190 OSORIO, GREGORIO

Letter addressed to Father Luis Morote. San Francisco de la Junta, New Mexico, June 17, 1715.

2 pp. 30½ cm.

Osorio, a Franciscan sent to New Mexico to convert the Indians, reports that many of them along the Rio del Norte are already Christianized and friendly to the Spanish. The others living in idolatry were easily converted and have erected the Holy Cross to replace their images.

[S–648]

191 PADEN, MELVIN, *d.* 1854

Correspondence. Various places, August 9, 1852–April 8, 1854.

18 pp. 23–27 cm. With addresses.

Life in the mine fields in and around Butte County, California, reflected in the correspondence of a prospector to his wife and a friend. A letter to Paden's wife from his brother telling of his death in the mine fields is included.

MORGAN, EVAN S. Letter to "Dear Jane," written on letter from Melvin Paden. January 8, 1853. 1 p.

PADEN, E. C. Letter to "Senora Jane Paden." Union Bar, Feather River, California, October 23, 1852. 2 pp.

—— Letter to Mrs. M. J. Paden. Rancho de la Laguna, Seco, California, April 8, 1854. 3 pp.

PADEN, MELVIN. Letter to "Dear Jane." Montgumerys [*sic*] Bar, Bute [*sic*] County, California, August 9, 1852. 2 pp.

—— Letter to "Dear Wife." [n.p.], November 9, 1852. 2 pp.

—— Letter to Jane Paden. Ofer Sity [*sic*], December 25, 1852. 3 pp.

—— Letter to "Dear Friends." Ofer [*sic*], California, January 8, 1853. 3 pp.

—— Letter to "Dear Wife and Children." St. louis [*sic*] or Clear Yes Digans [*sic*], June 8, 1853. 3 pp.

[S–717; P133]

192 PARKER, JAMES W.

Letter to "Dear Coz." New York, New York, January 16, 1848 [i.e., 1849].

2 pp. 32½ cm.

Describes the agreement under which he and two others are being sent to California on the bark *Mazeppa* to mine for gold and engage in any other endeavors that might produce a profit.

[S–718; P226]

193 PATERO, SEVERO

Letter describing the events which took place at Nootka Sound. Nootka Sound, Vancouver Island, July 13, 1789.

4 pp. 21 cm.

In this letter to an unidentified friend, Patero tells of the foreign ships coming to Nootka Sound—English, Portuguese, Russian, and American. An American ship commanded by John Kendrick is especially mentioned, as well as a brief description of the life and customs of the Indians in the area.

[S–621]

194 PATON, JAMES

Letter addressed to Henry Dundas. Bombay, India, December 1, 1785.

4 pp. 22½ cm.

Suggesting an expedition by the East India Company to the northwest coast of North America to secure furs for the China market.

[S–226; P274]

195 PEDRERA MASCARENAS, FRANCISCO ANTONIO

"Manifesto que defiende a la America en el año S^{to} de la suspencion general de las indulgencias plenarías." Zacetecas, Mexico, 1725.

49 pp. 21½ cm.

Relating to the suspension of indulgences in New Spain, a serious question among the religious groups working with the Indians, and what effect this would have on the missionary efforts in the Southwest.

[S–622]

196 PEÑA GERTRUDIS, MARQUESA DE LAS TORRES DE RADA

Description of the estate of Marquesa de las Torres de Rada. Mexico City, Mexico, September 5, 1753.

59 pp. 31 cm.

In her will, the Marquesa de las Torres de Rada left a large portion of her estate to the Pious Fund of the Californias. José Lorens, a nephew, contested the validity of the will. The present document includes a description of the estate and testimony as to the Marquesa's intentions.

[S–663]

197 PETTIS, GEORGE HENRY, b. 1834

Letters and papers, 1861–1865.

130 pp. 20–35 cm.

Letters to his wife, Annie. Pettis, a lieutenant in the California Volunteers during the Civil War, recruited and commanded Company K, 1st California Volunteer Infantry, under Colonel James H. Carleton, in its campaigns in New Mexico, Arizona, and Texas. Writing from most of the posts and towns in this area, Pettis gives an informal description of them, and also tells of the difficulties of frontier duty in a time of limited communication and erratic pay. Included are the descriptive rolls of the men recruited by Lieutenant Pettis, giving rank, age, size, description, place of birth, occupation, and enlistment date, with, in some cases, notation as to cause of death. Carleton's commission as Colonel of Infantry, California Volunteers, a calendar, and an incomplete typed transcript of the correspondence, are also included.

[S–711; P453]

198 ——, PHILO

Eight letters to and from Philo. Various places, April 4, 1850–September 16, 1855.

30 pp. 20–25 cm.

Dismissing the early part of his overland journey to California as relatively easy, Philo describes the extreme difficulties encountered by the emigrants traveling down the Humboldt River to the Sink and through the desert, often in deep sand. Other letters, both from and to Philo, describe the Wolf Creek mine regions, a cholera epidemic at Sacramento, living conditions at the mines, and the lives of those left at home by the prospectors.

BRITTAIN, S. A. Letter to "Friend Philo." San Jose, California, September 16, 1855. 4 pp.

"COUSIN DAN." Letter to "Mon cher Cousin." Tallmadge, Ohio, January 20, 1854. 4 pp.

PECK, SARAH T. and CHARLOTTE C. Letter to Philo. Tallmadge, Ohio, April 16, 1851. 4 pp.

PHILO. Letter to "Dear Parents and Sister." Near Hangtown, California, September 1, 1850. 3 pp.

—— Letter to "Dear Sister." Nevada City, California, November 10, 1851. 4 pp.

TRENT, NANCY. Letter to Philo. Tallmadge, Ohio, July 5, 1851. 4 pp.

TRENT, ORRIEL. Letter to Philo. Hudson, Ohio, April 4, 1850. 3 pp.

WRIGHT, BEN. Letter to "Friend Philo." Wolf Creek, California, June 20, 1852. 4 pp.

[S–713; P548]

199 POMEROY, EBENEZER W[ATSON], 1806–1861

Two letters to Mrs. Maria Pomeroy. Santa Fé, New Mexico, September to October, 1846.

5 pp. 19–24½ cm.

Pomeroy, a trader, was also sutler to Kearny's dragoons. His letters contain news of Kearny's California expedition and business conditions in Santa Fé.

[S–647; P771]

200 POND, HORACE RANSOM, 1824–1849

Correspondence and papers, 1849–1850.

45 pp. 22–55 cm. With addresses.

Dr. Pond, a member of the Green Mountain Mining and Trading Company, describes his voyage on the bark *William Ivy* to California by way of Cape Horn with a stopover at Rio de Janeiro. A newspaper containing an article concerning the circumstances of Pond's death in Sacramento is included, along with another newspaper that describes the voyage to California of a group that had intended to sail on the *William Ivy* with Pond's company, but went instead on the *Bonne Adele*. Also included are a copy of the Articles of Copartnership of the Green Mountain Mining and Trading Company listing the members and their addresses, and a letter of recommendation to Major H. W. Wessells in San Francisco.

[S–714]

201 POST, J. H.

Letter to the Reverend H. Winslow. Merced River, Mariposa County, California, January 5, 1853.

4 pp., docketed. 27 cm.

Reflecting the moral conditions in the California gold fields.

[S-715; P846]

202 PRINCE, WILLIAM E., *d.* 1892

Letterbooks. Fort Leavenworth, Kansas, and Santa Fé, New Mexico, 1845–1848.

2 vols. [i.e., 204 pp.]. 32 cm.

The Fort Leavenworth letterbook covers the period from July 30, 1845 to October 30, 1847 during which time Lieutenant Prince was Assistant Commissary of Subsistence at that post. It contains much information relating to the supply of Doniphan's and Kearny's expeditions, the Oregon Battalion, and other forces operating on the frontier.

In November 1847 Prince became Aide-de-Camp and Adjutant to Brigadier General Sterling Price commanding the newly created 9th Military Department, which included New Mexico. The second letterbook (unbound) contains his drafts of official correspondence relating to civil and military affairs within the Department, December 16, 1847 to January 3, 1848, together with some general and special orders.

[S–551]

203 PUERTOLLANO, YSIDORO

"Representacion al Rey en solicitud de dos ministros para la misiones." College of Pachuca, Mexico City, Mexico, April 20, 1793.

12 pp., 31 cm.

Missionaries trained at the College of Pachuca, Mexico, were sent out to the frontier, especially the provinces of Coahuila and Texas. As the priests were burdened with more than clerical duties, Puertollano appeals for additional help and funds to carry on the duties in each mission and spread the faith. For the results of this petition, see below, no. 230.

[S–654]

204 QUICKSILVER PROPERTY IN CALIFORNIA

Anonymous report [*ca.* 1860].

12 pp. 31½ cm.

Title from first sentence.

Concerning the quicksilver mines of California, particularly those on the Rancho Cañada De Los Capitancillos in Santa Clara County, and comparing the production from these mines to mines in other countries.

[S–786; Q4]

205 QUITMAN, JOHN ANTHONY, 1798–1858

Letter to Captain George T. M. Davis. Washington, D.C., April 8, 1856.

3 pp. 20½ cm.

A justification of Quitman's actions in the battle for Mexico City; his estimate of their effect on the outcome of the War.

[S–565; Q48]

206 RAMSEY, ALBERT C.

Three letters to Isaac V. Fowler. National Hotel, Washington, D.C., December 11, 1858–February 16, 1859.

10 pp., docketed. 20½ cm.

Ramsey, promoting a Vera Cruz, Acapulco, and San Francisco mail route, needs Fowler's help to get through Congress the bill appropriating funds for the enterprise. He feels that a word from Fowler, who was Grand Sachem of Tammany Hall and postmaster of New York City, would at least keep Senators Gwin and Slidell silent rather than voting against the measure.

[S–716; R149]

207 REDINGTON AND COMPANY, SAN FRANCISCO

Correspondence and papers, 1865–1870.

104 pp. 18½–35½ cm.

Correspondence mainly with its branch, Coffin, Redington and Company, New York. The company was the first wholesale drug firm in the area, but was notable for its diversity of interests, engaging in, among other things, mining of all types, including quicksilver, water power, and irrigation.

[S–697; R248]

208 RICHARDSON, ISRAEL BUSH, 1815–1862

Letter to his mother, Mrs. J. P. Richardson. Fort Jesup, Louisiana, July 30, 1844.

3 pp. 25 cm. With address.

Includes a discussion of the effect of the proposed annexation of Texas on United States troop movements in the South.

[S–567; R394]

209 RIO GRANDE (DISTRICT)

Copies of six letters from "Gef[a] politica del partido de Rio Grande" to "ayuntam[tos] de las villas del partido." Guerréro, Mexico, February 2 to June 1, 1847.

16 pp. 22–32½ cm.

Letters and petitions to the various districts in the Rio Grande asking the Mexican guerrillas to take up arms against the North Americans. The tactics they should adopt are outlined in eight articles.

[S–620]

210 RIVERA Y MONCADA, FERNANDO

Letter addressed to Antonio Bucareli y Ursua, Viceroy of Mexico. Loreto, California, November 12, 1777.

2 pp. 30½ cm.

A graphic account of the Indian attacks at San Juan Bautista, Mexico, on a group of Spanish soldiers who were en route to San Diego, California.

[S–658]

211 ROGERS, LESTER TINKER, *b.* 1821

Account of the discovery of gold in California, addressed to James S. Rogers. Milton Junction, Wisconsin [*ca.* 1880].

5 pp. 30½ cm.

Another version of the discovery of gold at Sutter's saw mill, avoiding the issue of who actually made the discovery, but attributing the confirmation of the material found to a Mrs. Weimer [i.e., Wimmer], and recounting the story of the group of Mormons working the mill. Also recounted is the alleged theft by Sam Brannan of the goods shipped around the Horn by Isaac Rogers, Jr., father of the author. There are other uncomplimentary remarks about the Mormons and their leaders.

[S–739; R6315]

212 ROGERS, LUCETTA (DENNIS)

Seven letters to Frank and William Eno. Various places, 1853–1882.

17 pp. 18–25 cm. With typewritten calendar.

A woman's view of a voyage to California by way of Nicaragua and of life in and around San Francisco. Sailing on the *Star of the West,* Mrs. Rogers finds the trip across the Isthmus pleasant, but the voyage up the coast on the *Brother Jonathan* full of misery. Other letters describe the Fraser River gold rush, damage done to her home by firemen, and climatic conditions.

[S–731; R632]

213 SAN BUENAVENTURA MARTINEZ DE TEJADA DIEZ DE VELASCO, FRANCISCO DE, *d.* 1760

Reports made by officials to the Bishop of Guadalajara after his visit to various missions in his diocese, and his action thereon. December 28, 1759, to March 26, 1760.

26 pp. 30–31½ cm. With transcription and translation.

Fourteen sworn affidavits from the priests and settlers in the Camargo area regarding the founding of the towns and missions, in order to determine whether the settlements came under the jurisdiction of the Bishop or of the missionary College of Zacatecas. In his report the Bishop empowers the missionaries to perform marriages and other acts pending decision by higher authority.

[S–655]

214 SAN FRANCISCO. CITIZENS

Petition to Governor Mason regarding the removal of George Hyde as Alcalde of San Francisco [1848?].

2 pp. 27 cm.

Asking for the removal of Hyde in the best interests of the town. Signed by John W. H. Drummond and thirty-two other townspeople.

[S–740; Sa523]

215 SAN FRANCISCO. TOWN COUNCIL

Five letters written by various people addressed primarily to William M. Eddy, Town Surveyor. San Francisco, California, 1850.

5 pp. 14–30 cm.

Concerning the surveying of city lots. Includes a notice posted in the public square as shown by the pin holes in the four corners.

[S–237; Sa52]

216 SAN FRANCISCO ACCUMULATING FUND ASSOCIATION

Various records of the Association, including the Constitution and By-Laws, 1854–1862.

207 pp. 32 cm.

The Association was created by the adoption of its Constitution on April 27, 1854, to provide a means "by which its members shall, out of its funds, obtain the capital necessary for the purchase of real estate, erection of buildings, redemption of mortgages and other similar purposes." In addition to the Constitution and By-Laws, this volume of records includes a register signed by the membership showing the number of shares each owned, an index of members giving occupations and place of residence, and registers of cancelled and assigned shares. Individual notes transferring shares are bound in.

[S–750]

217 SANTA ANNA, ANTONIO LÓPEZ DE, PRES. MEXICO, 1795–1876

Communications exchanged between General Santa Anna, the Government of Texas, General Vicente Filisola, and Texas Secretary of War, Thomas J. Rusk. San Jacinto, Texas, April 22–30, 1836.

5 pp. 21½–31½ cm.

Written after the Mexican defeat at San Jacinto where Santa Anna was captured by the Texans, these letters to his second in command, Vicente Filisola, contain orders for the withdrawal of troops from Bejar and Victoria, the release of Texan prisoners captured at Copano, and an armistice satisfactory to both Mexico and Texas.

Contemporary copies, accompanied by a brief listing and summary.

[S–768; Sa58]

218 SANTAREN, HERNANDO, 1565?–1616

Letter addressed to Father Rodrigo de Cabredo, Provincial de la compañía de Jesús. Mexico City, Mexico, January 1, 1616.

4 pp. 30½ cm.

Report made to his superior on the conversion of the Nevome Indians to Catholicism.

[S–771; Sa60]

219 SARGENT, LORENZO D., 1825?–1882

Journal, 1849–1850. Various places.

94 pp., illus. 20½ cm.

Sargent's journal describes his voyage with the Salem Mechanics Mining and Trading Company on the ship *Crescent* from Salem to San Francisco by way of Cape Horn and Juan Fernandez Island. Continuing his narrative upon arrival at his destination, he relates his experiences during the unloading of the ship,

Loreto 12 de Nov.e de 77.

El Ten.te de Gov.or
de Californias

Exmo. Señor

El 9 del corriente por la noche tuve correo con
carta de Monterrey, luego di providencia vi-
niesse de Puerto Escondido yna Lancha en la
q.e despacho ohas cartas á S.ta Cruz con or.n
de q.e el Arraez las lleve á entregar al R.r delos
Alamos.

Con las primeras cartas q.e vinieron del
s.or Com.te Gen.l pasaron quatro Soldados à
S.n Diego, hazia de Cavo Antonio Briones,
volvian ya, y estando parados haziendo noche
en el Paraje de S. Juan Bap.ta como 18 leg.
retirados de aquel Presidio, dicen q.e Ramon
Noriega se hallo de sentinela, q.e entretanto
daba yna vuelta alas mulas, les acometieron
los Gentiles, alos tres q.e dormian los hirie-
ron, pero de muerte solo al Cavo; seguia la
noche q.do los Gentiles se retiraron, y inmedia-
tamente se pusieron los Soldados en marcha
p.a S. Diego, no llego el Cavo, lo sepultaron en
el camino. Tengo noticia q.e el Alfer.z D.n Joph
Francisco Ortega practico dilig.s y dio quenta
al Gov.or D.n Phelipe de Neve.

Los dias 23, y 25 de Ag.to 1.o y 2.o de Septiem-
bre llovio aqui con algun excesso, el Quartel
en partes se hundio fue preciso en yn todo
quitarle el techo; y en lo perteneciente ala
casa en q.e vivo hizo mucho daño. No
ocurre otra cosa digna poner en aten-

9.   MS. No. 210   *Fernando Rivera y Moncada*

para aprill

quando subi ala sinaloa me pidieron los padres de
Rio adentro el p.e Villalta y el p.e Andres perez y
otro que quisasse encargarme del rio de los nebomes que pidiendo doctrina y estaban para darse
la pareçiendoles que no solo podria servir a
nro señor y aquellas almas con la gra qual el
señor me ha dado pa ayudar a esta gente nueba
sino que les podria servir a todos ellos en lo
que me ofreçieron que se negoçiasse con el
señor governador la casa del presidio y fuerte
que ellos juzgaban que fuesse caminando
con la doctrina que pareze tienen raçon pues
vienen a estar la villa gente a la lengua de los
nebomes y sesta el presidio como esta cerca la
villa de ordinario y pareçeles que yo podria negoçiallo con el señor governador
de manera que presto ellos me rogaron que
yo lo pusiesse y aunque les di mi palabra de
ponello yo lo he mirado y pensado despues
a cosomendado lo a señor muy despaçio
y pedido al p.e lo encomiende y despues
de haver pensado digo mi padre que yo me he
echo mas que lo que me lo mandara sin que
yo lo pidiera ni apuntara cossa alguna con
lo qual me pareçia que meramente lo echo

the details of selling the cargo, and his first impressions of the life and people of San Francisco. After one season in the mines in and around the Grass Valley and Deer Creek regions, he considers himself fortunate to have mined 69 ounces of gold, and returns to his home, becoming a member of the crew of the *Itasca* as far as Valparaiso, and of the *Prospero* from that port when the *Itasca* picks up cargo that must go back to San Francisco. A partial listing of the members of the company precedes the journal; pen sketches of views seen on the voyages illustrate parts of the text. A note dated August 1862 following the narrative and signed by his wife Harriet, records Sargent's death in the Civil War.

[S–790]

220 SCOTT, WINFIELD, 1786–1866

Letter to Major General Quitman. Headquarters of the Army, Puebla, Mexico, May 31, 1847.

4 pp. 23 cm.

Throughout the Mexican War Scott was harassed by rivalry among his subordinate commanders. This letter is an attempt at soothing the ruffled feelings of General Quitman who was aggrieved at not receiving a command commensurate with his rank.

[S–568; Sco86]

221 SHERMAN, WILLIAM TECUMSEH, 1820–1891

Letter to "My dear friend" [Lieutenant E. O. C. Ord?]. Camp on the American Fork, near Sutter's, California, October 28, 1848.

12 pp. 25 cm.

Desertions and the excitement of the rush for gold made a personal inspection by the Governor, Colonel R. B. Mason, necessary, and Sherman, as adjutant, accompanied him. This letter describes much of the route taken, the mining successes he found, living conditions in and around the mines, and a report on current prices. He discusses his business with N. S. Bestor and William H. Warner, and the trouble Sutter may have caused himself by deeding his land to his son. This letter, and the one following, were published as Mr. Beinecke's Christmas keepsake in 1964.

[S–742; Sh56]

222 SHERMAN, WILLIAM TECUMSEH, 1820–1891

Letter to "My dear friend" [Lieutenant E. O. C. Ord?]. Camp on the American Fork, near Sutter's, California, November 14, 1848.

8 pp. 25 cm.

Sherman continues his narrative of the inspection tour taken with the Governor, Colonel R. B. Mason, in this letter presumably to his friend, Lieutenant E. O. C. Ord. He discusses the geological aspects of the terrain encountered, describes the mining activities in the Stanislaus region, and after telling about the whereabouts of some mutual friends, he informs Ord to expect him back in Monterey soon.

[S–743; Sh56]

223 SHERMAN, WILLIAM TECUMSEH, 1820–1891

Post Orders No. 38. Headquarters, Monterey, California, July 23, 1848.

2 pp. 25 cm. With typed transcript.

As post adjutant under Colonel R. B. Mason, Sherman orders a detachment under Lieutenant E. O. C. Ord to pursue and apprehend Army deserters in the gold-mining regions.

[S–741; Sh56]

224 SHUART, JESSE H.

Correspondence and papers, 1850–1865.

476 pp., illus. 31 cm. With typed transcript.

Shuart's first letter tells of his voyage on the *Powhattan* as far as Bermuda. His other correspondence concerns the years spent in California, first in a search for gold and then through varying degrees of success as a farmer in Onion Valley, Calaveras County. He discusses in detail the ship and its officers, his stay in Bermuda, and his mining operations—with illustrations of some of his equipment. He also discusses the difficulties involved in acquiring full title to his land, a scheme to transport butter to California for profit, and the market fluctuations in the prices of his grain. The correspondence from his family is mostly personal in nature, reflecting life in Orange County, New York, and the effect of the rush to California on those at home.

[S–746]

225 SLATER, EMILY

Letter to "Dear daughter Adeline." Dry Creek, California, January 18, 1863.

4 pp. 20 cm.

A reflection of life in a farm home in Butte County, California, from the point of view of the woman pioneer.

[S–785; SL15]

226 SMITH, ABRAM, 1812–1854

Correspondence, 1852–1854.

171 pp. 12½–31 cm.

Abram Smith went to California on the steamships *New Orleans* and *Pioneer* by way of Panama. Instead of gold, he found only hard work with little financial reward. The correspondence is mainly with his wife, Samantha, but includes some letters from his daughters and friends. He describes not only his own experiences in traveling to California and working in the mines, but also those of many of their friends and acquaintances from Jefferson County, New York. Included are the resolution that formed the Jefferson Fluming Company on the North Fork of the American River, California, and a letter in a pocket letterbook, "designed to facilitate correspondence between cities and towns, and the mining districts of California," made and sold by D. Barnes of Middletown, Connecticut, in which is printed a description of Berford and

Company's Great California Express. Laid in is a newspaper clipping of a report on Smith's death in a landslide.

CAMPBELL, LESTER. Letter to Hiram Lanphear. December 1, 1854. 4 pp.

—— Letter to Samantha Smith. [n.d.] 1 p.

CAMPBELL, WAITE. Letter to Lanphear. January 11, 1854. 1 p.

JEFFERSON FLUMING COMPANY. Resolution of organization. Signed by James H. Ward, Milo G. Ford, Jacob Attley, Edward Hilton, Albert Hilton, Lester Campbell, Abram Smith, and Simon Maynard. July 7, 1853. 2 pp.

LAMB, CATHERINE E. Letter to Abram Smith. May 2, 1852. 1 p.

LANPHEAR, HIRAM. Three letters to Abram Smith. May 26, October 15, 1853; and [n.d.]. 10 pp.

LOOMIS, SALLY (SANDERS). Two letters to Abram Smith. July 11, December 18, 1853. 2 pp.

SANDERS, JOSEPH. Six letters to Abram Smith. September 10, 1852–January 27, 1854. 12 pp.

SMITH, ABRAM. Letter to Mrs. Sally (Sanders) Loomis. March 10, 1853. 3 pp.

—— Two letters to Lanphear. April 10, September 11, 1853. 7 pp.

—— Two letters to Sarah M. Smith. April 24, November 7, 1853. 1 p.

—— Four letters to Cledestine A. Smith. April 24, June 12, November 7, 1853; pocket letterbook [n.d.]. 37 pp.

—— Letter to Nelson Brooks. September 4, 1853. 1 p.

—— Letter to Lester Campbell. December 29, 1853. 1 p.

—— Thirteen letters to Samantha Smith. February 23, 1852–November 7, 1853. 31 pp.

SMITH, CLEDESTINE A. Nine letters to Abram Smith. May 2, 1852–February 6, 1854. 19 pp.

SMITH, SAMANTHA. Thirteen letters to Abram Smith. May 2, 1852–January 15, 1854. 36 pp.

—— Letter to Campbell. March 17, 1854. 2 pp.

[S–733; Sm51]

227 SMITH, ASA BOWEN, 1809–1886

Thirty-one letters primarily to various members of his family. New Haven, Connecticut and various places, 1837–1842.

118 pp. 25½ cm.

The letters describe his journey from Vermont across the country to Oregon where he worked among the Indians as a missionary under the supervision of Dr. Marcus Whitman.

Other correspondence is in the Coe Collection at Yale University.

—— Twenty-eight letters to his brothers, sisters, and parents, August 4, 1837–February 3, 1842. 112 pp.

U.S. BUREAU OF INDIAN AFFAIRS. Letter of transmittal and a passport for Smith. March 19, 1838. 2 pp.

WHITMAN, MARCUS. Letter to Smith. May 31, 1844. 4 pp.

[S–624]

228 SMITH, JOSEPH ROWE

Correspondence, letters, and papers, including military orders, 1846–1848; a diary written in 1847 and 1848.

100 pp. 18–32 cm.

Letters written by Captain Joseph Smith, 2d Regiment of Infantry, to his wife and other members of his family from Tampico and Puebla during the Mexican War. There are also two letters to Joseph from his brother, Henry Smith, who was stationed at Vera Cruz. The miscellaneous papers contain several extracts and requests for breveting Smith for his bravery at Cerro Gordo, Contreras, and Churusbusco.

Smith's diary gives detailed accounts of the positions, moves, and respective strengths of both armies.

SMITH, JOSEPH ROWE. Two letters to Louisa De Hart. October 24, December 8, 1847. 5 pp.

—— Five letters to Mrs. J. R. Smith. February 19–October 22, 1847. 22 pp.

—— Diary. 1847–1848. 44 pp.

SMITH, HENRY. Two letters to Smith. July 10, 16, 1847. 7 pp.

[S–571; Sm615]

229   SPAIN. ARMADA

"Dilig^s de embarco y conduc^n de cinco religios el orden de S^n Fran^{co} parte de una mision de veinte y cinco y dos legos consedida por S. M. p^a el Colegio Apostólico de Sta Cruz de Queretaro." Cadiz, Spain, July to November 1789.

21 pp. 21–31 cm.

Six documents concerning missionaries being sent from Spain. A list of the group, with a physical description of each man, is given, as well as an account sheet showing the cost of maintaining and transporting the missionaries to New Spain.

[S–610; Sp15]

230   SPAIN. SOVEREIGNS, ETC., 1788–1808 (CHARLES IV)

"Real cedula sobre aumento de un ministro en las misiones del Colegio Apostólico de Pachuca." Aranjuez, Spain, January 25, 1794. With additions, Mexico City, Mexico, September 19 and October 4, 1794.

6 pp. 31 cm.

Provides that missions established in New Spain by the College of Pachuca were to have an extra person to help the priest in his multiple duties as cleric, doctor, and educator. The eight communities of Texas were especially designated as being in need of additional help. For the petition from the College of Pachuca for this augmentation, see above, no. 203.

[S–627]

231   STANTON, EDWIN McMASTERS, 1814–1869

Letter to P. H. Watson. San Francisco, California, June 19, 1858.

3 pp. 20 cm.

Written while in California as special counsel for the federal government, this letter tells of the Fraser River gold rush and gives Stanton's views of its importance to the country. Peter Hill Watson was Stanton's confidant and legal partner for much of his life and served as Assistant Secretary of War under Stanton in Lincoln's cabinet. Reproduced in part in Frank Abial Flower's *Edwin McMasters Stanton.*

[S–735; St26]

232 STOREY, NELSON, 1858–

Letter addressed to Mr. Granville Stuart. Bozeman, Montana, June 15, 1918.

3 pp. 27½ cm.

An account of pioneer days in Montana, this letter tells of the burning of Fort Smith by the Sioux Indians and the great fire at Helena, Montana in 1879.

[S–223; St76]

233 STUART, JOSEPH ALONZO, b. 1825

"Notes on a trip to California, and life in the mines." Marysville, California, April 17, 1849, to December 6, 1853.

2 vols. [i.e., 206 pp.], illus. 21–25 cm.

A lengthy and detailed picture of travel and life in the mines. Stuart joined the Granite State and California Mining and Trading Company, organized at Boston in the spring of 1849. Combining with the Mt. Washington Company of the same city, they traveled to St. Joseph, Missouri, by rail and boat, and from there to California by pack mule. After two years in the mines, Stuart returned via Nicaragua to Lowell, Massachusetts, in the autumn of 1851. In December 1851 he set out once more for Nicaragua and California where he remained until September 1853. The manuscript, written partly from recollection and partly from his original diaries, is illustrated with pen and ink sketches and pictures clipped from various sources. A slightly different version appears in the author's *My Roving Life,* Auburn, California, 1895.

[S–619]

234 SUTTER, JOHN AUGUSTUS, 1803–1880

Letter addressed to "Lieutenant de Riviere, U.S.N." Nueva Helvetia, California, July 1, 1846.

1 p. 27 cm.

Joseph W. Revere, an officer on the sloop of war *Portsmouth,* visited Sutter in Nueva Helvetia, one week prior to the Bear Flag revolt in Sonoma. Sutter's letter is a request for paint and other supplies for the Bear Flag rebels.

[S–759; Su86]

235 SUTTER, JOHN AUGUSTUS, 1803–1880

Letter addressed to Colonel L. Sanders, Jr. Marysville, California, May 5, 1856.

2 pp. 25 cm.

Relates to a suit brought against him by Henry E. Robinson. A copy of Sanders'
reply is on the verso.   [S–234; Su86]

236 SUTTER, JOHN AUGUSTUS, 1803–1880

Letter addressed to Antonio Suñol. Nueva Helvetia, California, December 1, 1840.

1 p. 25 cm.

Acknowledging the receipt of supplies and ordering various seeds.

[S–758; Su86]

237 SUTTER, JOHN AUGUSTUS, 1803–1880

Letter addressed to "Monsieur le capitaine, J. J. Vioget." Hockfarm,
California, February 14, 1850.

1 p. 25½ cm.

Sutter wants to talk over the problem of squatters on his land with his Swiss friend, Jean Jacques Vioget, who had made the surveys.

[S–763; Su86]

238 SWIFT, WILLIAM H.

Journal, 1856–1858.

51 pp. 26 cm.

The diary contains entries from July 1 to September 5, 1856, January 11 to March 11, 1857, and February 14 to June 12, 1858, describing Swift's activities as a surveyor in Leavenworth, Kansas, and the struggle between the Free-Soil and proslavery parties.

[S–193]

239 TAMARIZ, FRANCISCO DE PAULA

". . . Real orden sobre que se examine una memoria que presentó al rey
el teniente de navio Don Francisco de Paula Tamariz sobre mejorar el
sistema de gobierno de la Alta California." San Fernando [California],
May 20, 1814.

59 pp. 21½–31 cm. Copy made in Mexico, January 29, 1815.

Tamariz, a naval lieutenant, extols the natural resources and economic advantages to be realized from the development of Alta California, or Nueva Albion as it was called. In his memorial to the King of Spain (Ferdinand VII), Tamariz mentions especially: development of the gold, silver, mercury, and iron mines; the fishing industry; whale and sea otter hunting; and trade in cowhides and wool, both valuable commercial commodities. Tamariz finds some of the missionaries' activities undesirable and is concerned about their power over the Indians. He recommends that the missionaries be sent to outlying districts and more families be brought into the territory to establish additional Spanish settlements.

Copies of letters which follow Tamariz' petition acknowledge the King's sanction for a commission of five to seven men, thoroughly acquainted with California affairs, to investigate the economic, mercantile, and religious potentials of Alta California, and a better scheme for governing the territory. This commission was the beginning of the Junta de Fomento de Californias.

[S760; T149]

240 TAMAULIPAS, MEXICO. GOBERNADOR (ACTING) 1835–1836 (SAMANO)

Circular sent to the Ayuntamiento of Jiménez from the acting Governor of Tamaulipas. Ciudad-Victoria, Mexico, August 29, 1836.

2 pp. 30½ cm. With heading: Gobierno del Departmento de Tamaulipas. Muy reservada.

Instructions for enlisting replacements for the Army of Operations against Texas.

[S–591; T151]

241 TAMAULIPAS, MEXICO. GOBERNADOR, 1835–1837 (FERNÁNDEZ IZAGUIRRE)

Three letters to the Ayuntamiento of Jiménez. Ciudad-Victoria, Mexico, October 16, 21, 1835, and November 16, 1836.

6 pp. 30 cm.

These letters give news of the rebellion of the Texas colonists and orders concerning mobilization of the militia for the defense of Matamoras and procurement of supplies for the Army of Operations against Texas.

[S–596; T1512]

242 TAYLOR, ZACHARY, 1784–1850

Twenty-three letters. Various places, 1844–1848.

64 pp. 24½–31½ cm. Some accompanied by transcripts.

In 1844 Taylor commanded the 1st Military Department, whose headquarters were at Fort Jesup, Louisiana. In the summer of 1845, after annexation of Texas to the United States, he commanded the "Army of Occupation" in that state and established his forces first at Corpus Christi and then on the north bank of the Rio Grande. War with Mexico began in 1846; for the first year Taylor was the major American commander in the field. His letters, official and personal, deal with these events and his political ambitions, which culminated in his election as President in 1848.

—— Letter to Richard T. Allison. February 12, 1847. 5 pp.

—— Letter to Commodore David Conner. February 15, 1846. 2pp. Signature only.

—— Letter to John Danforth. September 27, 1847. 1 p. Signature only. Accompanied by ALS and a copy of a report from Danforth to Thomas W. Williams concerning Taylor's nomination. June 20 and November 12, 1848. 2 pp.

—— Two letters to William Learned Marcy. February 2, 1846 and August 16, 1847. 3 pp. Signature only.

—— Letter to the Honorable James Knox Polk. March 1, 1847. 1 p. Signature only.

—— Letter to Henry K. Rayner. October 30, 1848. 3 pp. Signature only.

—— Eleven letters to the Adjutant General of the U.S. Army. October 1, 1844, to November 14, 1847. 31 pp. Signatures only.

—— Three letters to Robert C. Wood. July 16, 1846, to November 2, 1847. 11 pp.

—— Two letters to John Ellis Wool. July 14, 1847, to September 18, 1847. 7 pp.

[S–641; T219]

243 TEXAS (PROVINCE), GOBERNADOR, 1790–1799 (MUÑOZ)

"Relacion de los gastos erogados en la manutención y obsequio de doscientos cinquenta y dos yndios Comanches, Tahuaises Aguages, Tancahues y Tahuacanes que se han presentado à recivir sus regalos en dicho Presidio desde 1 de Enero de 1799, hasta fin de Abril y 1º de Mayo de 1799 hasta 27 de Julio del mismo año." San Antonio, Texas, 1800.

12 pp. 30 cm. In two sewn quires.

Account of expenses for gifts to Indian tribes presented by Gabriel Gutierrez, executor of the deceased governor, Gabriel Muñoz. Certified by Juan Bautista de Elguezabal, acting governor.

[S–599; T31]

244 THOMPSON, PHILIP R., 1812–1857

A description of the military movement of Company F, 1st Dragoons, from Cerro Gordo to Mexico City. Mexico, February to December 1847.

4 pp. 25 cm.

A brief account of the troop movements from Cerro Gordo to Mexico City along with a list of promotions and casualties in Company F, 1st Dragoons during the Mexican War.

[S–575; T386]

245 TOMLINSON, WILLIAM P.

Letter to John G. Spencer. Matamoras, Mexico, February 15, 1848.

3 pp. 46 cm.

Writing from a camp near Matamoras, Mexico, Tomlinson, a soldier in the 10th Infantry, writes to Spencer about the abuse, mistreatment, and injustice done to the soldiers by their officers during the Mexican War.

[S–579; T597]

246 TURNER, GEORGE RUNEY, 1828–1899

Journal of a voyage in the ship *John Bartram* from Boston to San Francisco. November 22, 1851, to March 28, 1852.

100 pp. 20 cm.

Turner, going to California for his health, worked his passage on the ship *John Bartram,* which left Boston in November 1851 and arrived in California in March 1852. The diary depicts the daily routine of a seaman, compares holidays aboard ship with those spent at home, and tells of the birds, fish, and atmospheric phenomena noted as the ship traveled south around Cape Horn and up to San Francisco.

[S–232]

247 TWIGGS, DAVID EMANUEL, 1790–1862

Letter to Colonel G. W. Hughes. Vera Cruz, Mexico, January 2, 1848.

2 pp. 27½ cm. With address.

General Twiggs refuses to authorize an expedition to Orizaba and Cordova since he does not have the troops to hold them and as he feels the only result would be guerrilla reprisals against any Mexicans who cooperated with the Americans.

[S–501; T922]

248 U.S. ARMY. ARMY OF MEXICO, 1845–1848

Extract taken from the notes of Captain Eaton, Aide-De-Camp to General Taylor, made by Leslie Chase, First Lieutenant, 2d Artillery. [Monterrey, Mexico, September 1846].

2 pp. 25–30½ cm. With copy in Spanish.

The terms of capitulation of Monterrey after the battle (September 1846) and the city's occupation by General Worth's division.

[S–594; Un312]

249 U.S. ARMY. ARMY OF MEXICO, 1845–1848

"Hd. Qrs. Army of occupation. Orders no. 79." Matamoras, Mexico, June 29, 1846.

1 p. 25 cm. Signed: W. W. Bliss, Ass't. Adj. Genl.

Announces the appointment of R. S. Garnett, 1st Lieutenant, 4th Artillery, as aide-de-camp to General Taylor, and orders a general muster of all units on the following day.

[S–510; Un312]

250 U.S. ARMY. ARMY OF MEXICO, 1845–1848

"Proclamation. The General in Chief of the forces of the United States, To the Inhabitants of Tamaulipas, Nuevo Leon and Coahuila." [Monterrey, Mexico, March 22, 1847].

3 pp. 25 cm.

Taylor complains that in spite of his humane treatment of Mexican citizens they have joined in guerrilla attacks on his supply trains and have murdered the teamsters. He is therefore levying fines on them equal to the value of the supplies destroyed. Contemporary manuscript copy in English.

[S–573; Un312]

251 U.S. ARMY. ARMY OF MEXICO, 1845–1848

Thirteen letters to the Alcaldes of Cadereyta and Linares. Monterrey, Mexico, May 4, 1847, to April 6, 1848.

13 pp. 22–25 cm. Title on slip case, "Mexican War Manuscript Letters 1847–1848."

On collection of taxes by the American Army of Occupation and requisition of mules for American supply trains.

[S–614]

252 U.S. GEOGRAPHICAL SURVEYS WEST OF THE 100TH MERIDIAN

Registers of correspondence, letterpress copies of letters sent, meteorological and topographical observations, photographs, etc., of the Wheeler Survey, 1871–1879.

Ca. 7,500 pp., illus. 12–41 cm.

The Wheeler Survey, officially called the Geographical Surveys West of the 100th Meridian, grew out of the Army's desire to resume what it felt was the topographical engineer's real peacetime function: the creation of maps featuring not only the geological aspects of the West, emphasized in civilian surveys of the time, but also man-made improvements such as roads, farms, mines, and villages, and the "conformation, obstacles and resources of the country," all so necessary to the military strategist. Commanded by Lieutenant George Montague Wheeler (hence the popular name), the survey first began in 1871 as an "exploration of those portions of the United States Territory lying south of the Central Pacific Railroad, embracing parts of eastern Nevada and Arizona," but which soon grew in scope in 1872 to a mapping of all of the United States west of the 100th meridian. The survey ended on June 30, 1879 when the bill creating the U.S. Geological Survey became effective, leaving much of its primary objective undone.

The collection contains letterpress copies of letters signed by Wheeler and other officers of the survey; registers of correspondence sent and received; records of meteorological and topographical atlas sheets; photographs of parts of the territory covered by the expeditions; and a typed calendar.

Register of correspondence sent January 1, 1872, to December 30, 1873. Indexed. Printed extract of Appendix EE of the Report of the Chief of Engineers to the Secretary of War is appended. 286 pp. 40½ cm.

Letters. Bound letterpress copies of letters sent February 2, 1872, to June 26, 1872. Incomplete index. Most appear in the Register of Correspondence Sent, January 1, 1872, to December 30, 1873. 297 pp. 30½ cm.

―――― Bound letterpress copies of letters sent February 1, 1873, to May 20, 1873 and May 7, 1878, to May 10, 1878. Most appear in the Register of Correspondence Sent, 1872–1873. Pages 2, and 448–452 are missing. 485 pp. 30 cm.

—— Bound letterpress copies of letters sent May 22, 1875, to October 28, 1875. Indexed. Laid in is a letter signed by G. M. Wheeler. Washington, D.C., October 28, 1875. 500 pp. 28 cm.

—— Bound letterpress copies of letters sent February 7, 1876, to May 12, 1876. Indexed. 750 pp. 29 cm.

—— Bound letterpress copies of letters sent May 12, 1876, to November 29, 1876. Indexed. 748 pp. 29 cm.

—— Bound letterpress copies of letters sent December 1, 1876, to March 21, 1877. Indexed. 494 pp. 28 cm.

—— Bound letterpress and pencil copies of letters sent March 22, 1877, to October 4, 1877. Indexed. 497 pp. 28 cm.

—— Bound letterpress and pencil copies of letters sent July 9, 1877, to September 11, 1877, from the field, and October 4, 1877, to February 19, 1878, from the Washington office. Primarily signed by Wheeler. Indexed. 657 pp. 32 cm.

—— Bound letterpress copies of letters sent primarily from the field, February 7, 1878, to October 17, 1879. Laid in are pencilled notes apparently made by Lieutenant Wheeler at various times, 1871–1872. 161 pp. 30 cm.

—— Bound letterpress and pencil copies of letters sent May 11, 1878, to September 23, 1878. Indexed. 490 pp. 30½ cm.

—— Bound letterpress copies of letters sent May 19, 1880, to December 3, 1880. Indexed. 448 pp. 28 cm.

Topographical atlas sheets, 1877. Printed to accompany Appendix NN of Annual Report of the Chief of Engineers, the annual report of Lieutenant Wheeler. Scale 1:253440 (1″ = 4 mi.). Indexed. On cover. 9 sheets. 49 × 61 cm.

Journal. Telegraphic Longitude Campaign of Lieutenant G. M. Wheeler's Exploring Expedition, 1871. Stations Carlin, Nevada, Battle Mountain, Nevada, and Austin, Nevada. May 10 to July 1, 1871. Lieutenant D. E. Lockwood, probable author. 70 pp. 22 cm.

Astronomical Records. Los Angeles, California, July 1 to Elizabeth Lake, October 25, 1875. Lieutenant C. W. Whipple, observer. 23 pp. 20 cm.

Field Journal. May 28, 1876, Carson, Nevada, to November 6, 1876, near Susanville, Nevada. 73 pp. 20½ cm.

Topographical Records. Books nos. 52, 55, 74, 93, 115, 131, 171, 200, 201, 224, 226, 271, 323, 384, 389, and 431 of the survey. 1872–1878. Including topographical sketches, odometer readings, triangulation, angle records, and topographical meanders. 16 vols., 25½ × 14–17 × 10 cm.

Computation of Geodetic Co-ordinates. Triangulation stations, 1878. Party 2, California, Lieutenant Macomb. 41 pp. 27 cm.

Meteorological Records. Books Nos. 10, 11, 17, 25, 26, 32, 42, 56, 76, 85, and 121 of the survey. Including field observations, aneroid profile computations, aneroid and odometer records, barometric hypsometry computations, and aneroid readings. 11 vols., 11 × 17–28½ × 26½ cm.

Letters received. Date of receipt and file number, date and subject of letter, and action taken on letters received. Engineer Office, Explorations in Nevada and Arizona, January 24–June 29, 1872; December 13, 1872–November 8, 1873; June 12, 1873–December 31, 1873; November 17, 1876–December 12, 1876; September 21, 1876; August, 1876; November 1, 1875–January 2, 1876. 301 pp. 40½ cm.

Photographs. Expeditions of 1871, 1872, 1873, and 1874. Fifty stereoscope views by T. H. O'Sullivan and William Bell, photographers. With explanatory text.

—— Showing landscapes, geological and other features, of portions of the Western Territory of the United States. Seasons of 1871, 1872, and 1873. Fifty photographs by T. H. O'Sullivan and William Bell, photographers. Bound. 40½ × 53½ cm. Generally duplicates the following.

—— Showing landscapes, geographical and other features, of portions of the Western Territory of the United States obtained in connection with Geographical and Geological Surveys West of the 100th Meridian, seasons of 1871, 1872, 1873, and 1874. With explanatory text.

Twenty-five photographs by T. H. O'Sullivan and William Bell, lithographed by Julius Bien. Bound. 51 × 43 cm.

—— Explorations in Nevada and Arizona, expedition of 1871. Sixteen photographs by T. H. O'Sullivan. 40 × 50½ cm.

—— Explorations and Surveys West of the 100th Meridian, expedition of 1872. 14 of 15 photographs by William Bell. No. 5 is missing. 40 × 50½ cm.

—— Geographical and Geological Explorations and Surveys West of the 100th Meridian, expedition of 1873. Nineteen photographs by T. H. O'Sullivan. 40 × 50½ cm.

[S–744]

253 U.S. QUARTERMASTER DEPARTMENT

Copy of a letter to Colonel Henry Stanton, Assistant Quartermaster General, from Lieutenant Colonel Aeneas MacKay. St. Louis, Missouri, May 22, 1847.

2 pp. 25 cm.

A board of survey at Camargo had condemned a large number of knapsacks and canteens as unfit for service. MacKay, the Department Quartermaster at St. Louis, denies that they were either procured or issued by him.

[S–553; Un38]

254 U.S. WAR DEPARTMENT

Letter from the Secretary of War, John B. Floyd, to the Colonel of Ordnance. [Washington, D.C.], August 11, 1858.

1 p., docketed. 25 cm.

Secretary of War Floyd authorizes the Colonel of Ordnance, Henry K. Craig, to sell arms and ammunition to Edward F. Beale, the superintendent of the wagon road running from Fort Defiance to the Colorado River.

[S–782; Un39]

255 U.S. WAR DEPARTMENT

Copy of letter from William L. Marcy, Secretary of War, to Colonel Richard B. Mason, 1st Dragoons. Washington, D.C., November 3, 1846.

3 pp. 32 cm. Unsigned.

Mason is ordered to proceed to California via the Isthmus and to report to General Kearny for duty. If Kearny has not yet arrived, Mason is to take command of all American land forces in the area and conduct operations there. Mason later became military governor of California after its seizure by the United States.

[S–514; Un39]

256 U.S. WAR DEPARTMENT

Draft of a letter from the Secretary of War, William L. Marcy, to Major General Winfield Scott, U.S. Army. Washington, D.C., May 19, 1847.

3 pp. 32 cm. With typewritten transcript.

A letter of congratulation for the American victory at Cerro Gordo. He also expresses his sympathy to the families and friends of those men who lost their lives in the battle.

[S–507; Un39]

257 U.S. WAR DEPARTMENT

Draft of a letter from W. L. Marcy, Secretary of War, to General Zachary Taylor. Washington, D.C., September 1, 1846.

7 pp. 25 cm.

The government is contemplating the seizure of Tampico and requests Taylor's views on the feasibility of the operation and its effect on the proposed advance to San Luis Potosí.

[S–556; Un39]

258 VALLEJO, MARIANO GUADALUPE, 1808–1890

Letter addressed to Manuel Castro. Sonoma District, California, [April] 1855.

1 p. 24½ cm.

Because of business conditions, Vallejo is not able to pay his debt to Castro, and berates the latter for his ungentlemanly attitude.

[S–765; V2422]

259 VARA CASTAÑEDA VILLAGRA, LORENZO

Petition and documents by the descendants of Gaspar de Villagra. Mexico City, Mexico, March 3, 1713.

180 pp. 31 cm. Bound in vellum.

Lorenzo Villagra requests a pension as a return for the services rendered by his ancestor, Gaspar Perez de Villagra, an associate of Oñate in the conquest of New Mexico, 1595–1599, and author of *Historia de la Nuevo Mexico* (Alcala de Henares, 1610). The petition contains a detailed account of Gaspar de Villagra's career in the New World.

[S–665]

260 VARO, ANDRES, 1683?

"Satisfaccion plena y docta dada contra las iniquisimas falsas calumnias presentados ante el Exm. S. Virrey por el Govr del Nuevo Mexico Thomas Velez Cachupin, Mision del Paso del Rio del Norte," New Mexico, February 5, 1751.

103 pp. 30 cm. Worn leaves affect some text.

Varo, a Franciscan, wrote on controversial subjects, especially in regard to the Church. He gives a very detailed account of the clash between the ecclesiastical and civil authorities. He points out that the civil authorities are bitter towards the missionaries and say that they have made the Indians steal sheep for them so that they can sell the wool to add to their own incomes. Varo states firmly that the Church only administers the Holy Sacraments when the Indians are dying, and then only by means of an interpreter. This account furnishes a good background for the early colonial history of New Mexico.

[S–644]

261 VERA CRUZ, MEXICO (CITY)

"Memoranda of campaigns in Mexico." Castle Loretto, Puebla, Mexico, August 8, 1847.

107 pp. 31½ cm.

A detailed account assembled by an unknown author of the siege and capture of Vera Cruz. The format of the material indicates that the author intended to publish the work. A list of commissioned and noncommissioned officers at the siege of Vera Cruz appears in the appendix.

[S–576; V581]

262 VERA CRUZ, MEXICO (CITY)

"Sitio y Toma de Veracruz por los Norte Americanos." Vera Cruz and Orizaba, Mexico, March 25 to April 12, 1847.

6 pp. 21½ cm. With two typescripts.

Report of the Comandante General of Vera Cruz to the Secretary of War on the siege and capture of the city by the Americans, with two other documents relating to the event.

[S–609; V581]

263 VIADER, FRAY JOSÉ

Letter addressed to Fray Juan Cortes. Santa Clara, [California, 1825].

2 pp. 18 cm. With typescript.

"Received August 31, 1825."

Fray Viader requests Fray Juan Cortes, Procurator of the College of San Fernando, to send the following religious items on the brigantine *Maria Ester:* the Stations of the Cross; large, good paintings for the rooms at the mission; and a quantity of paper and medical supplies.

[S–764; V6492]

÷ ꝰ Recꝺ agto. 31 ꝺ 825

Viva Jesus.

Querido Compañero ij Amigo P. Juan
Cortes. A mas de lo pedido á Dn Enrique Virmond
como lo verás en la carta que el mismo te entrega-
ra, se añade lo siguiente. Primo. Una Via Sacra ó
estaciones del via Crucis sin los marcos; sino puras
laminas grandes ij buenas. Ytm 6 campanas grandes
para salvos en las fiestas. Ytm 3 juegos de sacras
ó palabreros de Altar sin marcos, sino solo el pa-
pel.
Ytm las medicinas siguentes. Sublimado 2 onzas, mercuri-
ó dulce 2 onzas. estracto de saturno una botella.
Sal de Inglaterra pa purgas mediaꝺ, polvos de jalapa
una libꝺ. un bote de unguento de Altea. Ytm otro de A=
gripa. Ytm egypciaco. Aceijte violada. Emplasto de
cicuta. Cantaridas. Una bolsa instrumentos de ciru
jia, con dos jeringuillas chicas, ij dos grandes. Ytm 6 lan
cetas, las 3 de pico de gorrión, ij las otras 3 de oja de olivo.
Ytm opoven, en vasa, ij en pulpa. Ytm 6 libꝭ de
quina, ij una onza de opio. Ytm nadamas, que pa
san lo bien ij mandan á tu Compº Q B M.

F. Jose Viader

P. D. me dice el dador de esta Dn Enrique que el Sol
es mucho mejor que el Redactor, ij en este caso, seria
mejor subscrivirnos á lo mejor.

Vale #

11.   MS. No. 263   José Viader

consultar á S. M. sobre este particular.

Dios nro Sor que á

V. E. m.s a.s Colegio Apostolico de la Sta Cruz de
Queretaro, y Diziembre 24 de 18.8.

Exc.mo Señor

F. Jose Ximenez
Guardn

Mexco Diciembre 30 de 1808

Al S. Fiscal de R.l Hacienda con el asto relativo

en el estado que tuviere —

Mexino

Exmo Sor

El Fiscal de R.l Hac.a

Ex.mo sor Virrey
Dn Pedro Garivay.

12. MS. No. 285   *José Ximenez*

264 VILLA, ANTONIO MARÍA

"Rancho de Tequepis. Translation of Espediente." [n.p., n.d.]

3 pp. 30 cm.

Title from docket.

Copy of Villa's petition for a land grant and the subsequent administrative decisions of Governor Pío Pico and the Departmental Assembly in 1845 and 1846. The copy was made by the law firm of Halleck, Peachy, and Billings some time in the 1850s.

[S–512; V712]

265 WALDO, WILLIAM, 1812–1881

Three letters addressed to Mrs. Mary C. Ames, 1860–1861.

16 pp. 20 cm. With typescript.

Written on a 1,500-mile hunting trip through the mountains of Arizona, New Mexico, Mexico, and Texas. [S–229]

266 WALKER, BENJAMIN, d. 1858

Letter addressed to the paymaster general, Nathan Towson. Santa Fé, New Mexico, October 19, 1846.

2 pp., docketed. 25 cm. With address.

On provision of funds and appointment of J. H. Cloud as paymaster for Kearny's California expedition. [S–652; W151]

267 WARNER, WILLIAM

Letter addressed to his sister, Sarah Warner. Monterey, California, May 30, 1848.

3 pp. 25 cm.

News of the California gold discoveries and consequent gold rush.

[S–613]

268 WASHINGTON, JOHN MACRAE, 1797–1853

Letter to his wife. Monterrey, Mexico, June 5, 1848.

1 p. 25 cm.

In a brief letter to his wife, Washington tells of the "news of the ratification of the treaty of peace between the United States and Mexico."

[S–580; W2775]

269 WEISS, EMANUEL

Correspondence, 1849–1868.

20 pp. 20–28 cm.

Weiss was promoting the idea of using camels in the Southwest. This correspondence shows how he proposed to secure the animals and deliver them, the approximate cost of the venture, and the opposition to the plan by the Secretary of War, Jefferson Davis.

DAVIS, JEFFERSON. Two letters to Weiss. September 16, 1854 and July 19, 1855. 2 pp.

—— Copies of the above in Weiss' handwriting. 2 pp.

SKINNER, FREDERICK GUSTAVUS. Two letters to Weiss. December 12, 1849 and April 10, 1851. 2 pp.

—— Copies of the above in Weiss' handwriting. 3 pp.

WEISS, EMANUEL. Statement dated June 1867. 4 pp.

—— Undated statement attached to copy of letter from Jefferson Davis quoting parts of letters from F. G. Skinner and J. D. B. DeBow. 2 pp.

—— Letter to L. H. Phelps. October 10, 1868. 3 pp.

—— Copy of letter to Jefferson Davis. June 5, 1855. 1 p.

[S–737; W436]

270 WELCKER, GEORGE L., 1812–1848

Letter to E. O. C. Ord. Washington, D.C., October 28, 1847.

4 pp. 25 cm. With address.

Captain Welcker, serving as assistant to the chief engineer in Washington, writes to his friend Ord at Monterey with news of their many acquaintances. He comments about the court-martial of Frémont and the excitement caused by victories in Mexico.

[S–738; W448]

271 WERTZ, HENRY M.

Five letters to his parents and sister, April 7, 1850–February 9, 1854.

11 pp. 20½–25 cm.

Wertz, a member of the Wayne County Company, writes of some of his experiences in traveling overland with the company to California, adding to the information of the same journey in Keller's *A Trip Across the Plains*. Other letters tell of his purchase of, and experiences with, the river steamer *Comanche*, which he ran between Marysville and Sacramento, and of mining copper in the Nebraska, California area.

[S–734; W499]

272 WHITNEY, JOSIAH DWIGHT, 1819–1896

Letter to Joshua E. Clayton. San Francisco, California, February 2, 1874.

2 pp. 20½ cm.

Whitney, the California State Geologist at the time of this letter, refers to his fight to continue publishing the mining laws of the state, and offers to send Clayton one of his new maps of California and Nevada.

[S–788; W614]

273 WILKES, CHARLES, 1798–1887

Draft of a letter to Messrs. Gales and Seaton. Washington, D.C., June 8, 1848.

5 pp. 32 cm.

Draft of a letter to the editors of the *National Intelligencer,* which was published in that paper June 15, 1848. It continues correspondence begun by Senator Thomas Hart Benton in a letter published May 15, 1848, in which Benton had given credit for finding certain errors in the maps of the California and Oregon coasts to Lieutenant Colonel J. C. Frémont. Wilkes refuted much of what Benton said in a letter published June 8, 1848, and this letter further develops the points made at that time. In so doing, Wilkes describes the methods by which the coastline and the Sacramento River were mapped in his Exploring Expedition of 1838–1842, giving as a background some of the previous explorations made and the variations of their findings.

[S–732; W652]

274 WILSON, HENRY

Correspondence, military orders, and papers of Colonel Henry Wilson. Various places, 1829–1858.

186 pp. 16–33 cm. With manuscript map showing the route of the 1st Regiment of the U.S. Infantry, and the mule paths in Mexico, 1846.

Wilson commanded the 7th Infantry during the Mexican War. The bulk of these papers relate to his duties as military governor of Vera Cruz after its capture by the Americans in 1847. The letter from his daughter, Cecile V. Wilson, to Mrs. Cruzat, summarizes Wilson's military service from 1813 to 1851.

—— List of officers, commissioned and noncommissioned, and privates of the 4th Brigade, 1st Division, Army of Occupation, killed, wounded, and missing at the storming of Monterrey, September 21 and 22, 1846. Signed by Wilson. Copy. 4 pp.

—— List of ordnance and ordnance stores, pertaining to the post, received at Fort Smith, Arkansas by Wilson. May 31, 1855. Copy. 4 pp.

—— Petition to Congress, 1829. 2 pp.

—— Letter to Robert J. Atkinson. August 9, 1856. 1 p.

—— Letter to Adjutant General [Samuel Cooper]. February 7, 1857. 1 p.

—— Letter to General Roger Jones. May 12, 1845. Copy. 2 pp.

—— Letter to Brigadier General Roger Jones. October 17, 1847. 3 pp.

—— Letter to Colonel Francis Lee. October 1857. 1 p.

—— Two letters to Major Irvin McDowell. July 13, 1858 and August 31, 1858. 2 pp.

—— Letter to "My Dear General." December 13, 1854. 2 pp.

—— Letter to "My Dear Sir." July 2, 1847. 2 pp.

—— Letter to "My Dear Sir." September 1, 1847. 2 pp.

—— Letter to Major General Patterson. November 17, 1847. 3 pp.

—— Letter to Colonel L. Thomas. July 1, 1856. 1 p.

—— Letter to Colonel Thomas. March 31, 1859. 1 p.

BEARD, J. A. Letter to Wilson. September 15, 1847. 1 p.

BROOKS, EDWARD J. Letter to Wilson. March 24, 1856. 1 p.

BRUTUS, T. Letter to His Excellency, the Governor of Vera Cruz. [n.d.] 2 pp.

CALDWELL, GEORGE A. Letter to Wilson. June 19, 1847. 2 pp.

CHRISTY, WILLIAM. Letter to Wilson. April 26, 1847. 1 p.

COOPER, SAMUEL. Letter to Wilson. July 22, 1847. 2 pp.

DANIELS, JOSEPH. Letter to Wilson. April 29, 1847. 1 p.

GAGHAN, DENNIS. Report on the coaches being robbed. [n.d.] 3 pp.

GARDENIER, JOHN R. B. Letter to Wilson. May 3, 1847. 3 pp.

GARDNER, W. M. Letter to Wilson. April 26, 1847. 2 pp.

GATES, WILLIAM. Letter to Wilson. July 31, 1847. 2 pp.

HETZEL, ABNER R. Letter to Wilson. June 27, 1847. 2 pp.

HITCHCOCK, ETHAN ALLEN. Copy of letter to the commanding officer at Vera Cruz [Wilson]. April 19, 1847. 2 pp.

—— Letter to Wilson. May 15, 1847. 1 p.

HUGHES, GEORGE WURTZ. Letter to Wilson. September 10, 1847. 4 pp.

JAMES, GEORGE F. Letter to Wilson. April 28, 1847. 3 pp.

JESUP, THOMAS SIDNEY. Letter to Wilson. April 3, 1858. 2 pp.

LALLY, FOLLIOT T. Three letters to Wilson. August 9–September 30, 1847. 4 pp.

LARNED, BENJAMIN F. Letter to Wilson. July 27, 1847. 1 p.

PILLOW, GIDEON JOHNSON. Letter to Wilson. June 14, 1847. 2 pp.

QUITMAN, JOHN ANTHONY. Letter to H. L. Scott, and referred to Wilson. April 28, 1847. 2 pp.

SCOTT, HENRY LEE. Letter to Wilson. May 3, 1847. 3 pp.

SCOTT, WINFIELD. Copy of letter to Wilson. April 23, 1847. 4 pp.

SMITH, [C.] H. Letter to Wilson. July 12, 1847. 3 pp.

SMITH, HENRY. Letter to Wilson. July 4, 1847. 1 p.

SUMNER, EDWIN VOSE. Letter to Wilson. February 22, 1858. 1 p.

THOMAS, GEORGE HENRY. Letter to Wilson. June 21, 1846. 1 p.

TITUS, JONATHAN P. Letter to Wilson. June 25, 1847. 1 p.

VERA CRUZ, Board of Health. Letter to Wilson. June 5, 1847. 1 p.

WALSINGHAM, F. L. Letter to Wilson. October 12, 1847. 1 p.

WILSON, CÉCILE, V. Letter to Mrs. Heloise Hulse Cruzat. [n.d.] 3 pp.

[S–584; W694]

275 WILSON, JOHN S., *b.* 1830

Journal, March 21, 1859–November 25, 1860.

94 pp. 21½ cm.

A journal of an overland journey to California from Wheeling, West Virginia. Wilson was originally a part of the rush to Pike's Peak, but emigrants returning from there with stories of misfortune made him change his mind and head for California by way of St. Joseph, the Oregon Trail, Salt Lake City, Ogden, the Humboldt River, and finally to Yreka via the Honey Lake Road. He describes conditions on the trail, encounters with the Indians, and, upon his arrival in California, the life he found as a prospector. The latter part of the journal is an account of a trip by horse and pack toward Washington Territory. But difficulties on the trail and no success in finding gold force his party to turn back after only reaching and pros-pecting the Rogue River Valley in Oregon.

[S–795]

276 WINDELER, FREDERICH FRANZ ADOLPHUS

Journal, 1849–1853.

83 pp. 18½ cm. With manuscript transcript and 107 pencil sketches.

Windeler, a native of Hamburg, sailed for California on June 22, 1849 as a member of the crew of the ship *Probus*. He describes in detail the condition of the ship; the relations between crew, officers, and passengers; and the many details of the operation of a vessel during a voyage around the Horn to San Francisco. After reaching the Golden Gate, he works unloading ships until he and eight others organize a venture into the mining regions to seek gold. The remainder of the journal describes his day-to-day mining and prospecting activities, with two account books laid in showing the income and expenses of variously-named mining ventures. Also laid in are pencil sketches of scenes described in the journal, some of which might be attributed to his friend, Carl Christendorff.

[S–748]

277 WITHERS, WILLIAM T.

Five letters to his cousin, Doctor Montgomery W. Boyd. Camargo, Monterrey, Mexico, 1846–1847.

18 pp. 25–27 cm.

While he was serving as 2d Lieutenant in the 2d Regiment of Kentucky Volunteers and as Aide-De-Camp to Brigadier General Thomas Marshall during the Mexican War, William Withers wrote to his cousin telling him about the military moves of the various state regiments, and the military plans of Generals Patterson, Taylor, Wool, and Santa Anna concerning Camargo, Monterrey, Saltillo, and Buena Vista. According to Withers, it was highly important to occupy Vera Cruz in order to march on Mexico City.

Besides the military information given in his letters, Withers gives an excellent description of the natural beauty of Monterrey and a minute description of the Mexican house in which they were quartered.

[S–581; W776]

278 WOOD, SAMUEL SMITH, 1799–1881

Four letters to his wife, Mary Ann Wood. San Juan del Norte, Nicaragua, and San Francisco, California, March 18, 24, 27, and November 27, 1849.

11 pp. 25½ cm. With address.

Traveling to California with the Gordon Association, Wood describes San Juan del Norte, Nicaragua, as he impatiently awaits transportation across the Isthmus. He laments the harsh treatment and poor conditions suffered during the voyage. Another letter tells of his fruitless attempts at mining and of his success as he turns to trading.

[Historical Manuscripts Collection]

279 WOODWORTH, FREDERICK AUGUSTINE, *d.* 1865

Letter sent to George P. Morris, editor of the *New York Mirror*. San Francisco, California, July 1, 1851.

5 pp. 29 cm.

Describes robberies and vandalism in San Francisco in detail, formation of the Vigilance Committee, and the execution of the notorious criminal John Jenkins.

[S–616]

280 WOOL, JOHN ELLIS, 1784–1869

Letter addressed to Colonel John J. Abert. Monterrey, Mexico, January 3, 1848.

3 pp. 25 cm.

Wool denies that Captain G. W. Hughes had picked the field for the battle of Buena Vista, claiming the credit for himself.

[S–642; W88]

281 WOOL, JOHN ELLIS, 1784–1869

Letter addressed to Joseph W. Moulton. Buena Vista, Mexico, May 20, 1847.

2 pp. 25 cm.

Wool writes his views on the significance of the battle of Buena Vista to Joseph W. Moulton, a lawyer friend in New York.

[S–902; W88]

282 WOOL, JOHN ELLIS, 1784–1869

Letter signed by John E. Wool, Brigadier General, U.S. Army, to General Zachary Taylor. Buena Vista, Mexico, January 20, 1847.

7 pp. 25 cm. With typescript.

A long and involved account of friction between Wool, General Worth, and General W. O. Butler. Wool complains of Butler's highhanded treatment of him and appeals to Taylor, their common superior, for justification.

[S–649; W88]

283 WORTH, WILLIAM JENKINS, 1794–1849

Letter to Major John Munroe. Point Isabel, Brazos St. Iago, Texas, April 13, 1846.

1 p. 31 cm.

Requests that Major Munroe fortify the supply depot even at the expense of delaying the re-embarkation of seamen.

[S–582; W899]

284 WORTH, WILLIAM JENKINS, 1794–1849

Four letters to his wife. St. Augustine, Florida and Corpus Christi, Texas, November 4, 1844–December 6, 1845.

15 pp. 25 cm. With typescripts.

One letter mutilated, affecting some text. Written just before the outbreak of the Mexican War, the letters give information on American troop movements and dispositions in Texas.

[S–583; W899]

285 XIMENEZ, JOSÉ

Letter addressed to the Mexican viceroy, Pedro de Garibay. Queretaro, Mexico, December 24, 1808; the Viceroy's reply, January 6, 1809.

7 pp. 29–31 cm.

Ximenez, guardian of the Apostolic College of Santa Cruz de Queretaro, sums up the hardships and the burden of the work carried on in the missions. He requests that more missionary bases be established along the Gila River, where there are many heathen Indian tribes.

The Viceroy replies that there will be more help than in the past, and that bases will be set up.

[S–661]

INDEX